Busy this
Evening?

Busy this Evening?

Yarns of a London Minicab Driver

CHRIS BASTIN

The Book Guild Ltd

First published in Great Britain in 2023 by
The Book Guild Ltd
Unit E2 Airfield Business Park,
Harrison Road, Market Harborough,
Leicestershire. LE16 7UL
Tel: 0116 2792299
www.bookguild.co.uk
Email: info@bookguild.co.uk
Twitter: @bookguild

This work is entirely fictitious and bears no resemblance
to any persons living or dead. Does have several references and
scenarios of real celebrities.

Typeset in 11pt Minion Pro

Printed on FSC accredited paper
Printed and bound in Great Britain by 4edge Limited

ISBN 978 1915853 035

I dedicate this book to my late mum, Elsie.
Thank you, Mum, for encouraging me to have a go in life.

Contents

Chapter One

The Laws of the Universe

Over the years, I have come to the realisation that there is a pre-ordained cosmic order to life.

Some cases in point:

a. Whenever I pick up a particularly nasty passenger poised on the edge of their seat waiting for any excuse to explode:

   i. This will be a long-haul job.

   ii. The trusty satnav, which never lets me down, will suddenly lose internet connection and we end up going miles out of the way.

b. As a man walks past his neighbour washing his car, he has no choice but to shout over, "You can do mine next."

c. Regardless of whether or not we have actually ever been there, when someone tells us that they are from Cornwall – "Aw, it's beautiful down there. If we had the weather, you wouldn't want to go anywhere else" – rolls straight off the tongue.

d. When a guy from the South Coast of England, up to the age of forty-two (forty-five and a half in Portsmouth), is walking down the High Street on a Saturday afternoon with his girl, and she links arms with him, immediately, his shoulders pull back, his chest puffs out, his arms splay and his fists clench, as his gait transforms from a stroll to a bowl, and a scrunched-up hardman – 'Don't mess with me, I'm with my girl' – grimace appears on his face!

e. The passenger with the halitosis will:
    i. Always sit in the front passenger seat.
    ii. Be the chattiest.
    iii. Afford you the respect of turning their head to face you when talking.
    iv. Refuse a mint when subtly offered.

f. When city folk go for a drive in the countryside and they see a horse, they exclaim, "Horse!"

g. Virtually every black cab driver you come across is called either Geoff or Jeff.

h. When I'm running late for a pick-up from Eurostar, St Pancras International Station, and have a banging headache from fighting through the rush-hour traffic and sprinting frantically from the car park to the meeting point:
    i. The train is at least half an hour late, and
    ii. The spirit of Les Dawson is being channelled through some hard-of-hearing old boy sitting at the public piano that has been conveniently plonked just outside the Arrivals doors. With great gusto, and coming up only for the occasional intake of air as he acknowledges the smiling passers-by with a nod, he reels off the

full catalogue of '60s and '70s hits, including *Spanish Harlem*, *What Now My Love*, *Don't Sleep in the Subway* and rounding off, of course, with *(Is This the Way to) Amarillo*.

Against such forces, reasoning, complaining and resisting are futile – submission is our only option!

Chapter Two

Welcome Aboard

Hi, guys, my name's Thomas Buckley.

Born and raised in Beckton, East London, I now live with my lovely wife, Helen, and our three amazing kids, Toby, seventeen; Charlotte, fifteen and Mathias, twelve, in Hornchurch, Essex.

On 15th May 2008, I commenced work as a minicab driver for one of London's leading people-carrying providers, where I have happily remained to the present day.

With all the interesting encounters I have in the course of my work, so many people over the years have suggested to me that I write a book about the life of a London minicab driver. A great idea, but I never really took it too seriously. That was until about two and a half years ago when I picked up Mary, a retired children's author. We had a lovely chat about the world and his wife, and I spun off a few of my favourite, well-rehearsed driving anecdotes.

At the end of the journey, Mary said to me, "I'm not quite sure how much you've been pulling my leg for the past half-hour, but you've certainly made me laugh with your 'yarns'. You must put these stories down in a book. I, for one, would love to read them, and I'm sure they will put a smile on many people's faces."

I tried to argue with her – "I'm a minicab driver, not a writer"... "I'm no good with words"... "I'm really slow on the computer"... "Who wants to listen to me babbling on?"... blah, blah, blah – but she wasn't having any of that, and made me promise that I make a start straight away, providing her with regular updates so that she could check in on my progress and provide me with any support I needed. As a man of my word, I had no choice, especially as she said that if I didn't, and she ever saw me again, she'd box my ears!

Well, Mary, you asked for it!

So, if everyone's ready, buckle up, let the journey begin!

Note: In order to minimise any offence, whilst retaining an element of authenticity, I have replaced all strong expletives with the word '*dashington*'.

Chapter Three

Thank You for Your Custom, We Know You Have a Choice

At its essence, the job of a minicab driver is to transport people from A to B as quickly and safely as possible. Creating the optimum, positive and enjoyable journey experience for the passenger, on the other hand, is a far more challenging proposition, requiring the application of a range of finely tuned social skills.

Reading the signs

Key to this is being sensitive to the dispositions of individual passengers. Some passengers, for example, are naturally outgoing and strike up a conversation with you immediately they get into the car, and by the end of the journey you're on each other's Christmas card lists. Others may be more reserved, or have things on their minds, or work to do on the way, and the last thing they need is a well-intentioned, over-enthusiastic driver in their earholes. To test the water, I will often casually throw out the odd tried and tested conversation starter from the trusty, old, imaginary minicab book of small talk – "Looks like rain. What's the forecast for the weekend?"… "What do you think of these climate change activists?"… "Are you keeping up with all the Brexit shenanigans?"… "Who've West Ham got this week?"… "Soon be Christmas!" From their response, I am generally able to assess my approach for the remainder of the journey.

As well as being responsive to social cues, observing the thousands of passengers that have sat in my car over the years, my powers of perception have developed to the point that I can now virtually write the script for many of the scenarios that unfold before me.

Whenever I am picking up late at night from a work function, for example, and I see a guy helping a pretty, tipsy, young lady (that he has clearly been desperately trying to impress all night) into the back seat, I know, without fail, that he is going to say something to me along the lines of:

"You've got very valuable cargo on board here, Driver. Make sure you get her home safely, or you'll have me to answer to."

Or, in the case of the three very pleasant, upbeat personal assistants:

PA 1: I know what I meant to say. Do you have any dealings with Melvin's PA, Simone Harvey-Johnson?

PA 2: Yeah, I think she's really nice. I get on really well with her.

PA 3: Me too. And she's so stunning.

PA 1: Especially with that flawless complexion. It's to die for.

7

PA 2: She's like a porcelain doll. I'm so jealous.

PA 3: I think we all are. And that soft, sultry voice.

PA 2: Yeah, it even makes me tingle when I hear it.

Yes, we all agree she's very nice, very attractive and very sensual. Wait for it. Okay, here we go – 5,4,3,2,1…

PA 1: But, have you noticed how abrupt she can be at times?

PA 2: Yeah, I asked her to do something urgent for one of Mike's big Japanese clients the other day and she said she couldn't because she still had ten minutes left of her lunch break.

PA 1: *Lunch break* – What is this strange word you use?

PA 3: She's done that sort of thing to me in the past as well. I reported it to Rod, and he spoke to Melvin, but Melvin won't have a word said against her.

PA 2: That's because she flutters those big fake eyelashes in his face all the time, and he just melts like a lovestruck teenager.

PA 1: I'm surprised she can even lift her head up under the weight of them.

PA 2: And that's not the only big fake things she flutters in his face either.

PA 3: Sorry, Jen, but I think you'll find they're real.

PA 2: Rrrrhhh.

PA 1: And how she manages to squeeze into those blouses and skirts beats me.

PA 2: Just because you can, doesn't mean you should.

PA 3: I heard she sprays them on every morning.

Laughter all round.

PA 1: But seriously, girls, we need to stand together on this one. I think we all need to go to our bosses and tell them that she doesn't fit in, and, for the sake of the organisation, something needs to be done about her right away.

PAs 2 & 3: Agreed.

You can't judge a book by its cover!

I would like to think that I'm an open-minded kind of guy that affords every passenger an equal level of courtesy and respect. That doesn't mean, however, that I don't make an instant judgement about them – *Seems like a jolly chap... Wouldn't like to meet her down a dark alley... Bit ditsy, how on earth did she ever manage to land a job like that?* From years of experience, however, I can tell you for sure that our instincts in this respect are not always to be trusted.

I once picked up an aristocratic lady from a luxurious mansion apartment block in Victoria to take her to her country estate in Surrey. Having kept me waiting for well over twenty minutes, a very elegant-looking woman in her early eighties finally appears at the front door and begins walking, bolt upright, at a snail's pace towards the car with an expression on her face like she has just sucked on a lemon. I'm thinking to myself, *Here we go, class divide! The arrogance. She's not rushing for nobody. I'm just something to be scraped off the bottom of your shoe! This is going to be a fun journey!* When she, at last, reaches the car, she apologises profusely for keeping me waiting and explains that she has only recently been discharged from hospital following a serious spinal operation to correct a curvature. Now a widow, she had been the wife of one of the UK's top industrialists, and lived on a country estate,

9

the likes of which you would see in a period drama. You know what, she was one of the kindest, gentlest ladies you could wish to meet, and we had a lovely chat all the way down to Surrey. One of the things that impressed me most about her, though, was just how interested she was in me and my life story. When I said that I liked to play a bit of snooker in my spare time, she told me that she loved the game, and that her husband had tried teaching her to play on the billiards table in the games room in the St Augustine Wing. She had even once managed a break of 17! Since the passing of her husband, Edgar, in May 2011, she hadn't played but loved to watch the UK and World Championships on television and found the clicking of the balls in the background very relaxing whilst reading in the parlour room. She was a massive fan of 'The Rocket', Ronnie O' Sullivan – 'Poetry in motion'… 'Prolific breakbuilder'… 'The consummate cueman'… 'Sheer genius'… 'The greatest player to ever grace the baize' – and will never forget that amazing 147 break in just five minutes, twenty seconds, which will probably never be beat.

So, having spent one and a half hours in the company of this lovely lady – who incidentally gave me a nice £20 tip for 'making it such an enjoyable journey' – in the immortal words of the mighty Rex from *Toy Story*, 'Great, now I have guilt'.

Our innate tendency to formulate judgements based upon first impressions is, perhaps, never stronger than when we meet someone who looks very much like somebody we know. Because of the physical similarities, we automatically assume that they have the same personality traits. But when the two characters are polar opposites, this can lead to very conflicted emotions within us. I remember picking up a man who was the absolute double of one of my secondary school* teachers, Mr Mott – a tall, lanky man with a mop of curly, mousy hair and noticeably protruding front teeth. Now, Mr Mott was a cynical, sarcastic man that had been at the same school far too long. For some reason, he had it in for me from day one, taking every opportunity he could to try to humiliate me in front of the class. When he would call the register, for example, it would be – "Jane, Mark, Glynn, Michelle, Buckley, Kim, David…" Even years later, when I would be down the gym punching the living daylights out of the boxing bag, I would be visualising Mr Mott's face on it, and give it an extra hard whack! Unsurprisingly, when this 'carbon copy' of a man that I had detested for so long got into the car, some powerful, negative feelings were awakened, and I took an instant dislike to him. The thing was, though, this gentleman was friendly, open and upbeat, and, within a minute or so, I felt relaxed and comfortable in his company as we jokingly set about putting the world to rights. I nodded and laughed at his quips, as he did mine, and I can honestly say this was one of the most enjoyable encounters that I can remember. Apart, that is, from the fact that, all through the banter, as I glanced periodically back in the rear-view mirror at this gentle-natured, cheerful, smiley man, all I could think was *I want to punch you in the face and stamp on your big toe!*

* Secondary school wasn't a particularly pleasant experience for me. I would regularly be called hurtful names like 'pimply face' and 'big ears'. And the kids could be just as nasty at times!

Note to self – 'Keep your gob shut and mind your own business'!

Unless it is something particularly inappropriate or offensive, it is not my place as the driver to comment, express an opinion, or pass judgement on anything that I might see or hear from my passengers. Easier said than done!

On one occasion, I had to take a businessman from central London to a conference centre just outside Baldock in Hertfordshire. He was an amiable, easy-going, down-to-earth guy, and we exchanged pleasantries for about ten minutes before he had to jump on a conference call with his American offices in Wisconsin and Idaho, which lasted the remaining forty-five minutes or so of the journey. They were discussing the global marketing strategy for his company's new range of bathroom suites, and after every point he made he would conclude by saying, in a slow, drawn-out way,

"If... that... makes... sense?" – with the upward inflection on sense!

Now, this guy was an excellent communicator, expressing himself succinctly and articulately. In fact, even I could understand what he was conveying, so his American colleagues would have had no trouble at all. After about the fourth point, this really started to grate on me. My mind became preoccupied – *Oh no, he's about to round the point up. Please, please don't say it, I beg of you, I'll do anything!*

And then out it came:

"If... that... makes... sense?"

By point sixteen, I could feel my stomach churning and my nervous system on the brink of going catatonic. All I could think of was pulling over into the lay-by, getting out, opening the back door, grabbing his lapels, shaking him about like a rag doll and shouting in his ear:

"Yes… it… makes… perfect… *dashington*… sense!"

Somehow, I managed to muster every bit of strength within me – *Must… re… sist* – and was just about able to restrain myself. Two more points max, and the story could have had a very different ending!

However, when we pulled up at the venue and the guy wrapped up his conference call, he said to me that he was a little surprised that we hadn't taken the direct route straight up the A1 to Baldock. After explaining that there had been an accident on the A1, so I had rerouted round the M25, up the M1 and across the A507, with that infernal drawn-out phrase still revolving around in my head, I heard myself say to him,

"If… that… makes… sense?" – with the upward inflection on sense!

Fortunately, he didn't seem to twig, and just thanked me for getting him there safe and sound and on time, before going on his merry way, rejoicing.

Another time that I only narrowly avoided interjecting into a private passenger conversation was when I picked up a couple of young executives from a well-known international domestic supplies company:

Jamie: Did you hear about what happened to Len?

Daryl: No, pray tell.

Jamie: This hasn't come from me, okay, and you cannot say a word to anybody, understood?

Daryl: Lips sealed.

Jamie: Well, you know there's been these sophisticated email scams doing the rounds, right?

Darly: Don't tell me Len's been spoofed?

Jamie: Big time, man!

Daryl: Spill.

Jamie: Well, apparently he got an email from 'Jasper' in Dublin saying that he was working on the launch of a major new product that was going to completely revolutionise the domestic cleaning industry. For security, everything was highly classified and on a need-to-know basis, with everyone having to maintain radio silence at all times. Nobody could discuss anything about it at all with anybody else, either within or outside the company. All communication was to be with just Jasper himself, and via that email address only.

Daryl: Go on.

Jamie: Well, after a couple of weeks of back and forths, Jasper then says he needs a financial contribution from each of the head offices in the nine countries for the 'Big Product Launch' and gives him the details of a specially designated 'Launch' account to transfer the money into.

Daryl: No, man, don't.

Jamie: Yeah, and you remember last week when he booked the Friday off?

Daryl: Yeah, that's right, he was all a bit guarded about it.

Jamie: That's because he went over to Dublin for the launch.

Daryl: Ouch, ouch, ouch!

Jamie: And ouch again. When he asked the receptionist for directions, she said she didn't know anything about any 'Big Product Launch' and told him that Jasper was on holiday for two weeks with his family in the Seychelles.

Daryl: Oh no, anybody but Len, he's always such a stickler for detail and procedure. He's probably the most honest *dashington* I've ever worked for. The *dashingtons*! He's a good man and doesn't deserve that.

Jamie: No, he doesn't, but these *dashington*s are ruthless, man. They couldn't give a flying *dashington* about the lives they destroy in their wake.

Daryl: What sort of money are we talking about here, Jame?

Jamie: BIG bucks, man. Look, mate, you've got to get to your meeting. We'll have a drink after work and I'll fill you in some more.

As they were walking off, I literally had to clamp my tongue with my jaws to stop myself from calling out, "Jamie, man, wait up. You can't leave me hanging like this! How much exactly is BIG bucks? Are we talking hundreds, thousands, millions here, what? And how did they get Len's email address in the first place and know so much about the business that they could fool him like that? Was it an inside job? Have they mounted an investigation? Len won't get fired, will he? It could have happened to any of us! Please, I can't bear it, I need to know!"

Note: One thing that really winds me up is when passengers are chatting away normally and, in my head, I'm going *Really, um, yeah, yeah, that's interesting, you don't say, carry on.* Then, suddenly, they'll come to a juicy bit, and will start whispering. It's so annoying having to crane my neck!

Alas, there have been a number of occasions when my tongue-biting powers have failed me, as in the case of the man and woman professors from the Faculty of Classical

Arts, Imperial College, London. Immediately they got into the car, they launched into a discussion about the merits of a recent article about unicorns. Both agreed with the assertion that the hair of the unicorn would have been used as an ancient antidote for poison. However, there was hot debate between the two of them on the contention that the horn of the unicorn, traditionally considered to be either plain white or gold, could well have been multi-coloured, and most probably variegated stripes. I may not have qualifications* coming out of my ears (that said, I recently came across my Achievements folder in the attic, where I found my Scout's *Camp Cook Badge*, my *Fifty-Yard Breast Stroke Certificate* and, one that I remember with great fondness, my *Graduation from Pencil to Pen Award*), but I do consider myself to have a modicum of intelligence. So, having endured this verbiage for the best part of fifteen minutes, when we finally reached our destination and they began alighting, I felt compelled to spin round and tell them both straight, "Sorry, but there is absolutely no way that you can possibly know that – unicorns have been extinct for millions of years!"

> * It's my older brother, Ray, that's the brains of the family. He graduated uni with a degree in Philosophy, Politics and Plumbing.

And then there was the time I collected a lovely young couple, Juliet and Clarke, from a restaurant in Covent Garden, where they had been celebrating Juliet's twenty-eighth birthday. I drove them to their home in Balham, South London, picking up their two-year-old daughter, Mia, from Juliet's mother in Streatham along the way. They were both very friendly and we chatted away about the demands of balancing work and family life. Twenty minutes or so into the journey, Clarke suddenly begins commenting on the previous weekend's *Strictly Come Dancing*, and how he couldn't believe that Craig only gave Stacey and Kevin's American Smooth a 9. This went on for the best part of ten minutes until we reached Juliet's mother's house. Whilst Juliet went in to get Mia, I couldn't hold it in, and turned around to Clarke and said:

"Clarke, man, what you playing at?"

Clarke: What do you mean?

Me: Talking about *Strictly* like that.

Clarke: I love the show. It's the highlight of my weekends leading up to Christmas.

Me: We all do, mate. But men cannot admit to their wives that they enjoy it, and we definitely can't let them know we understand the slightest thing about the dancing. It will kill your cred stone dead if you carry on like that, son, trust me! No, as far as she's concerned, you can't tell a Viennese waltz from a Walnut Whip. It's all just a complete blur to you and you're watching it under duress, and only because you love her and know she likes the two of you watching it together.

Clarke: Sorry, man, you're right. What was I thinking? I've let the side down, big time. What can I do?

Me: Right, first things first, don't panic. There's no real harm done at this stage. The show's only a few weeks in, so it's still salvageable.

Clarke: Yeah, but how?

Me: Right, you've got to phase it in gradually. Otherwise, she'll get suspicious. So, normally you'd be sitting down in the lounge together waiting for *Strictly* to start, right?

Clarke: Right.

Me: Well, this Saturday, as she's settling down to watch the show and waiting for you to come in and join her, you've got far more pressing things to attend to, like oiling the rabbit hutch hinges or organising your garden hose accessories, and come in about five minutes after it's started. Next week, you walk in about ten minutes late, and say 'Not this rubbish again,' and gradually build, as necessary, over the coming weeks. When she says, 'But I thought you enjoyed *Strictly*,' you say, 'I watch it because I know you love it, and I love you.' She'll love that, and, done right, within no time, you'll both be back on the couch together enjoying the whole show again, but, this time, with your cred intact! Right, so what have you got to do?

Clarke: Phase it in.

Me: You've got it, lad. Good luck.

Clarke: Thanks, man. I really appreciate that.

Me: No problem. And just quickly, because I think that's your wife and littl'un coming out. I know Craig can be a mean so-and-so at times, but on this occasion, yes, it was an amazing dance, but he was absolutely right. There were slight *gapping* issues. And also, in my opinion, which, surprisingly, none of the judges seemed to pick up on at the time, to have merited a 10, it needed a little bit more *Rise and Fall*.

Although I try my darnedest to keep my counsel when it comes to my passengers, there is one area in which I feel no compunction at all about pulling them up – and that's swearing! In my day, it was generally the men who swore, and, then, only in select company. Young guys are probably still slightly worse (they think they're being all tough and rebellious),* but these days everybody seems to be at it, and if you don't like it, then you can go and take a *dashington* running jump! Well, I, for one, don't wish to listen to selfish dimwits spewing out their profanities at will, without the slightest consideration for those around. On more than one occasion, I have pulled over, politely asked the passengers to alight, respectfully explained to them that I do not appreciate such talk in my car and then told them to *dashington* off out of it!

> * Don't get me wrong, I was no angel as a lad, and Saturday nights would often find me congregating with the rest of the local teenagers round the alleyways at the back of the houses sniffing Sellotape!

King Solomon would be proud of me

Although just a humble minicab driver, I am often called upon for advice, and occasionally to arbitrate in disputes.

Shortly after picking up a couple of young newlyweds,* the wife suddenly bursts into tears:

Young wife: Boohoo, boohoo. Your mum thinks I'm a terrible wife. I can't even make a proper shepherd's pie.

Young husband: Technically, it was a cottage pie, darling, because it was beef not lamb.

Not helping, lad.

Young wife:	Boohoo.
Young husband:	Mum thought the shepherd's pie was delicious. Didn't she say it was browned off to perfection? The only comment she made was that she, personally, always melts cheese on top of *her* shepherd's pie.
Young wife:	And you prefer it with cheese on, don't you?…Well?
Young husband:	Well, um…
Young wife:	You know I'm allergic to cheese – it gives me panda eyes. [*I hear bull's milk can be very good for that!*] And not just that, I've made you shepherd's pie at least three times before, so why have you never even mentioned that you prefer it with melted cheese on? Just let me think everything was all right.
Young husband:	Because it's not an issue. I love the way you make it.

Good recovery.

Young wife:	We've been married for six weeks now and I feel I don't even know you. What other secrets are you holding from me? You should have married Natalie. And you would have got a lot more than cheese on top, that's for sure.
Young husband:	Don't be silly, darling. You're the one that I love and want to spend the rest of my life with.
Young wife:	But I'm not sure if we are even compatible anymore.

| Young husband: | Sorry about this, Driver. What can I do to reassure her? |
| Me: | Well, speaking as someone with many years of marriage under his belt, when you are in love, as you two clearly are, you will obviously want the best for each other. And you will find that, over time, without even realising it, you will just naturally tune in to one another's needs. And, from my experience, the key to a really successful marriage is embracing the differences between each other. When you can do that, your relationship will be that much richer and more fulfilling. And when it comes to the shepherd's pie, I suggest you make two smaller ones, one with and one without the melted cheese on top. |

Smile and big cuddle to make up.

Young husband:	Thank you, Driver.
Young wife:	Yes, thank you so much. You're like a wise old sage.
Me:	Wise old sage and onion, more like.

Chuckle, chuckle.

What I also suggested was that, for a change down the line, they might want to try sprinkling some broken-up plain crisps on top of the mash before browning off, to give it a lovely crunchy texture. And, if they really wanted to spice things up in the kitchen department, they might like to experiment with some paprika crisps. But they've got plenty of time for all that sort of thing!

* Seeing those two newlyweds just starting out on their journey together got me thinking back to when I first met my Helen. A chum of mine, Mack, had been dating a girl who was heavily into her amateur dramatics and had managed to get him hooked. He kept banging on at me about how much fun it was and how I should come down and give it a go. Believe it or not, I was a professional boxer at that time (some of you might remember me by my ring name – *The Canvasback Kid*!) and told him that I needed to be totally focused on my boxing career and, well, all that sort of thing wouldn't exactly do a lot for the old fearsome warrior image! Mack wasn't taking no for an answer, though, and, in the end, I agreed to go along just the once to shut him up. When I walked into that hall, they were in the middle of rehearsing a musical production of *Robin Hood and His Merry Men*. (I still have nightmares about those tight green tights to this day!) It goes without saying that I felt like a fish out of water and resolved, there and then, never to return again. But at least I could say to Mack that I'd tried it out and it wasn't my thing, and hopefully get him off my back. That was until Maid Marion, aka Helen Moore, hurriedly appeared from behind a tree to inform Robin that the evil Sheriff of Nottingham had thrown Friar Tuck into the castle dungeon

for treason. I stood there transfixed. The loveliest creature I'd ever seen, she took my breath away! Halfway through the scene, the stage manager, standing in the wings, shouted a prompt to her in a deliberately comic tone that sent her into a fit of giggles, setting off a chain reaction amongst the rest of the cast on stage and bringing the scene to a grinding halt. I remember this strong, uncontrollable wave of jealousy coming over me – that this tall, dark, buff young man and his impossibly handsome face with its shimmering, flawless complexion could have such an entrancing effect on this amazing, beguiling young woman that I had never even set eyes on before. (I needn't have worried!) Her face alight with laughter, I was immersed in a beautiful warm glow, every care and worry I had dissipating away into the ether. I wished I could have been suspended in that moment for an eternity. Even today, of the seven billion smiles there are in this world, Helen still has my favourite, and every time I look into those beautiful soft sky-blue eyes, I am carried off into a warm summer's day with the sun's rays gently caressing my shoulders, the innocent sound of children's laughter, and Scottie dogs catching frisbees on the seashore. (Woah, woah, woah. What's going on here? All this mushy, slushy stuff. I have a reputation to think about, you know!) And as her hair glistened under the fluorescent glow of the stage lighting, she looked astonishingly like one of the characters out of the original 1970s series, *Charlie's Angels* – Bosley!

(Phew! That's better. I was getting a bit worried there for a minute!) Personally, I wasn't much cop at all the old acting lark, but for the next six months, every Wednesday evening I'd be down there, regular as clockwork, helping out on the technical side. At first, I don't think Helen even noticed me, but I used to work it so that I would be around at the breaks and position myself near to her and her group of friends. Gradually, I started saying the odd thing to her and after a while sensed that a little bit was coming back my way. Helen was an aspiring actress, and I overheard her say to a couple of friends that she had her first professional audition that coming Friday for a principal role in the West End production of *Beauty and the Beast* at the Adelphi Theatre, Strand. I casually said that I was free on Friday and would be more than happy to drive her up, to which she readily agreed. On the way, she told me that her agent had already sent her photographs to the casting company, and, off the record, they thought she had the perfect look for the part, and was the strongest of the three main contenders. So, as you can imagine, Helen was very excited. This could be her big break and launch her West End career. Unfortunately, however, I wasn't used to driving up town and inadvertently took the wrong turning, taking us miles out of our way, where we hit major roadworks and then got stuck behind the longest funeral cortege I've ever seen. When we finally arrived at the venue an hour and a half late, they were packing away and the role of the

Beast had already been cast. As you would expect, Helen was devastated and barely spoke a word all the way back home. I felt absolutely dreadful; her big break and I'd ruined it for her! Why hadn't I planned the route better? Why hadn't I insisted on picking her up earlier in case something like this happened? Idiot, idiot, idiot! I resigned myself to the fact that I'd blown any chance I may have had with her big time, and was kicking myself for the rest of the week. If it hadn't been for the fact that the group was only a matter of weeks away from their end-of-year production of *Annie* and I had a key technical role, which they wouldn't be able to replace at such short notice, I would probably never have gone back. When, however, the following Wednesday evening, I did eventually pluck up the courage to gingerly walk back into that church hall, bloodshot red in the face, my heart thumping ten to the dozen and my head gushing, I held my head down and sheepishly tried to slip past Helen unnoticed, fully expecting to get both barrels if she saw me. However, as I was walking past, she grabbed my hand and gave me that beautiful 'ray of sunshine' smile and a big hug and kiss on the cheek. Twenty-seven years and three kids later, and the rest is history, as they say! But that is Helen. That's her nature. She has no room in her heart for grudges. She sees the best in everybody. In fact, she is the kindest, warmest, softest, gentlest, most loving person I have ever known. And although she would tell me off, because she was so lovely, when we were dating, I just couldn't help lavishing her with gifts – chocolates, perfumes, jewellery. I'll never forget the look of joy on her face our first Christmas together, when I bought her a box set of her three all-time favourite movies – *Gone with the Wind*, *The Sound of Music* and *Return of the Living Dead 3*. This year's Christmas present didn't go down so well, though. I thought she'd be really pleased with a 'No! No! Pro'!

Note: Marital harmony tip for newlywed men: Fellas, early on in your marriage, it is very possible that you will encounter this scenario. Your lovely new wife will be on the phone for about an hour and a half to her mother talking about everything from her lumbago flaring up again to the thrilling finale of *Celebrity Chase*. When your wife is beginning to wrap the call up, and you're thinking to yourself, *Great, now we can snuggle down and enjoy the rest of the evening together*, and she says, "Okay, Mum, I'll be round in about twenty minutes," do yourself a massive favour – don't say anything and just put the football on!

Deep breath and count to ten

Every so often, I pick up a passenger that is just plain nasty and sits there, poised, waiting for the most trivial of excuses to explode, like arriving thirty seconds late, the internal temperature a degree or two off, hitting a shallow pothole in the road, or stopping off en route whilst I quickly nip out and pick myself up a few groceries for the week.

Trying to assess the best way of handling difficult passengers in the heat of the moment is never easy. In many ways, I guess, the response is very much an individual decision, as my chat with one particular driver clearly illustrates.

He recounted the time when he had just started in the minicab business some twenty-five years back. Working out of a cab office in Chadwell Heath, Essex, he had received a job to pick up a young couple late one Saturday night from a pub in Collier Row. The man was very drunk and abusive to him, saying that he wasn't driving fast enough, so he wasn't going to pay his fare. Finally, the driver had had enough, stopped the car, got out, walked round to the rear passenger side, dragged the man out, flung him to the tarmac and proceeded to punch him in the head and kick him in the ribs, telling him that he could keep his *dashington* eight quid. He left the man reeling in a pool of blood, with his girlfriend screaming hysterically. At the end of his shift, he dropped by the cab office and mentioned to the controller what had happened earlier. The controller advised:

"You shouldn't *r e a l l y* have done that!"

For me, wherever possible, the most successful approach to defusing a tense situation is always to remain calm and non-confrontational and, where appropriate, gradually talk the person round. I once picked up a lady, clearly dripping in wealth, from her home in Belgravia to go to the Royal Opera House, Covent Garden, to see *The Nutcracker*, a present from her grandchildren for her seventieth birthday. Unfortunately, it was early-evening rush hour and I hit a tonne of traffic and ended up arriving seven minutes late. She went absolutely ballistic at me, telling me how incompetent I was and that she was never going to use my company again, and would make sure as many people as possible knew about it. After giving her space to vent and catch her breath, I very subtly began turning on the old 'Buckley Charm'* (that diamond-encrusted antique brooch really did draw out those beautiful, big, round, piercing blue eyes!), and before she knew where she was, she'd transformed into the sweetest lady you could wish to meet, and even gave me a £2.50 tip for such a pleasant journey experience.

* Even though my boys are still quite young, I have felt it incumbent upon myself to begin instilling in them the need for caution when it comes to employing the old 'Buckley Charm', especially with ladies of a particular 'vintage' – that stuff's lethal!

There is just one occasion that I can remember when a passenger almost tipped me over the edge and I very nearly lost it with him.

I picked up a guy in his early thirties from the Lyric Theatre, Shaftesbury Avenue. He'd just been to see *Thriller* and was absolutely buzzing with excitement when he got in the back:

Man: Ah, wow. What a show. Michael Jackson is the greatest entertainer that has ever lived.

Me: Yeah, he certainly was something special.

Man: The best ever, man. Nobody else even comes anywhere near!

As he said this, I could feel a battle starting to rage within me:

I can't have this! Just let it go and move on! But someone's got to put this guy straight, for his own sake! It's not your place, leave it! But if I don't, who else is going to? The man has had a fantastic evening, so don't go spoiling it for him with a silly argument! But!'

Me: Totally agree.

(*Shall I? Shan't I? Shall I? Shan't I?*)

Me: If you take Elvis out of the equation, of course, that is!

Man: Michael's music had real soul, man, because he wrote all his own songs, but Elvis Presley relied on other people to write his stuff for him.

Me: True, but Elvis single-handedly revolutionised music and changed the face of popular culture forever. All the greats – Lennon, McCartney, Dylan, Clapton – pay tribute to how much they were influenced by him. 'Before Elvis, there was nothing'.

Man: But the electricity Michael had on stage with that beat and those dance moves – it was explosive.

Me: But Elvis could sing anything – rock 'n' roll, gospel, country, blues, folk; whatever he wanted. Michael Jackson just did pop.

Well, this Michael Jackson vs Elvis Presley exchange continued for the best part of the journey to Finchley, with both of us becoming increasingly assertive and animated in expressing our point of view. The tone remained respectful, however, until the guy hit me with, "If it wasn't for his looks, Elvis Presley would have been nothing but a glorified pub singer!" I could feel my demeanour visually change at this point as the rage started to well up inside of me. I think he must have realised that he'd pushed it too far and could get chucked out of the car, because he suddenly became very conciliatory – "These things are very subjective"… "It's all a matter of personal taste"… "It would be a boring world if we all liked exactly the same things." He was right, of course. The guy then deftly redirected the conversation on to the upcoming Le Mans Grand Prix, which certainly softened the tension for the remaining fifteen minutes or so of the journey. I thought at the time that this showed great form on his part. I did also feel a little ashamed, I must confess. I had at least ten years on this guy, so I should have been the mature one, the peacemaker, in this situation, rather than trying to force my preference on a complete stranger!

When we arrived at the guy's house, his parting comment to me as he was shutting the car door was:

"Michael's estate made $170 million dollars last year. Elvis Presley's made $55 million. I rest my case!"

RRRRRhhhhh. I won't lie to you; I was so livid that I seriously contemplated slipping back to his house in the middle of the night and dropping a massive stink bomb through his letter box. Fortunately, I put on a bit of *Love Me Tender,* which managed to calm me back down.

Chapter Four

We're a Motley Bunch, Us Lot

The nature of my job affords me the unique opportunity of meeting people from all different nationalities, backgrounds and walks of life. In all their shapes and guises, love 'em or loathe 'em, they are a constant source of fascination to me.

The human satnav

One thing that never ceases to amuse me is despite us successfully navigating often exceptionally difficult road conditions and incorporating sneaky little dodges known only to the most seasoned of drivers, when we arrive to within a quarter of a mile of their destination without a single glitch, a large number of passengers cannot help but furnish me with the last few directions:

"Okay, Driver, see the BP garage? Hang a right

immediately after that. Now start slowing down, I'm hundred yards up on the left. Just in front of that orange Dyno-Rod van would be lovely."

This could mildly irritate me if I let it, but I know they mean well, so I politely thank them, think happy thoughts and comply.

There is, however, a small group of people with an in-built GPS system that can really stretch this 'compulsion' to its limits. By this, I am referring to retired lorry drivers.

One such person was the gentleman I took home to Birmingham from St Bartholomew's Hospital, EC2. As we were busily chatting away, around the St John's Wood, NW8 area, engrossed in the conversation, I inadvertently overshot a turning. From this point on, I was directed every step of the way right up to his front door:

Gentleman: Don't worry, Driver, take the next turning on the right, Blomfield Road.

Me: Will do, thank you.

Gentleman: No problem... but apparently my blood count level's a bit on the low side... Right, Driver, you're gonna wanna take the next on the left, Warwick Avenue.

Me: Will do, thank you.

Gentleman: No problem... I've got to go back in six weeks... Right, Driver, in a couple of hundred yards, turn right onto the A404, Harrow Road.

Me: Will do, thank you.

Gentleman: No problem... I got my first job in a mill when I was fourteen... Right, Driver, in about half a mile, turn left onto Lord Hills Bridge.

Me: Will do, thank you.

Gentleman: No problem... When I was twenty-five, they

offered to pay for my HGV licence... Right, Driver, about a hundred yards up, you're doing a left into Gloucester Terrace.

Me: Will do, thank you.

Gentleman: No problem... I've travelled all over the UK, the continent, Holland, Belgium, you name it... Right, Driver, a few hundred yards up, you're merging onto the A40, Western Avenue. Keep on that road for about fourteen miles and then keep right onto the M40.

Me: Will do, thank you.

Gentleman: No problem... I met my Shirley at a local dance in 1953... Right, Driver, just keep following the signs to Birmingham.

Me: Will do, thank you.

Gentleman: No problem... She wasn't sure about me at first, because I was a bit of a tearaway back then... Right, Driver, so in a minute, you're gonna wanna be merging onto the M42.

Me: Will do, thank you.

Gentleman: No problem... We were national foxtrot finalists in 1955, narrowly losing out to Len Goodman and his partner, Maggy... Right, Driver, when you come to Junction 2, take the A441 exit to Birmingham.

Me: Will do, thank you.

Gentleman: No problem... Four daughters and five grandchildren later... Right, Driver, at the roundabout, take the third exit onto the A441 towards Birmingham.

Me: Will do, thank you.

Gentleman: No problem... My little four-year-old

grandson, Jeffie-boy, wants that taxi board game for Christmas... Right, Driver, at the roundabout, take the second exit onto the A441, Redditch Road.

Me: Will do, thank you.

Gentleman: No problem... I don't mind them playing on these FIFA games things, as long as they go over the park and have a proper kickabout with their mates... Right, Driver, again, at the roundabout, take the second exit onto the A441, Redditch Road.

Me: Will do, thank you.

Gentleman: No problem... My dad started taking me to watch Birmingham City when I was about seven years old, but these days the average family can't afford it... Right, Driver, at the roundabout take the second exit onto the A441, Pershore Road.

Me: Will do, thank you.

Gentleman: No problem... I don't know how you drive in London these days... Right, Driver, at the next roundabout coming up, you want the second exit onto the A441, Pershore Road.

Me: Will do, thank you.

Gentleman: No problem... That's what they reckon, but there's no way on this earth you're getting me in one of those driverless cars, I can tell you that for nothing... Right, Driver, same again, second exit at the roundabout onto the A441, Pershore Road, and I'm up on the left just before the Beefeater.

Me: Will do, thank you.

Gentleman: No problem.

If you'll excuse me, I'm just going off to take a box of Anadin and have a little lie-down for a couple of days!

For their incredible fortitude
Every so often, I will meet somebody whose conviction and courage truly humbles and inspires me.

One such person was a woman in her mid to late fifties that I collected from the World Wildlife Trust head office in Woking, Surrey late one evening to drive back to her home in West Sussex. Although her long, wavy, silver hair was a little unkempt, and she wore no makeup to enhance her beauty, I was instantly captivated by her stunning, strong but gentle features, and melted by the warmth of her tender smile.

As we talked, she shared with me how, at the age of twenty-eight, she had given up a lucrative career as an international fashion model to devote her life to the study and protection of the orangutan in Borneo. Since returning to the UK in 2014 to become an ambassador for the World Wildlife Trust, she has lived on a little half-acre homestead on the South Downs with her alpaca, Snedley, and sells her free-range potatoes, spring onions and cucumbers to local greengrocers in the surrounding villages, in order to support a largely subsistence-level lifestyle.

She told me that she was a naturalist, but unfortunately for me, it was mid-January, so she was fully clothed at the time!

As we talked about the issues facing our planet and its wonderful wildlife, I told her my personal observation (and indeed conflict) of how, when watching a David

Attenborough documentary on a Sunday afternoon about, say, a particular type of fish that needs to spawn by a certain time before the currents change for the year, we all root for the fish to evade its predators. ("Watch out, he's behind you!") But then, the following week, when watching another David Attenborough documentary about, say, a puffin that has to find food in order for its hungry newborn chicks to stand a chance of survival, we all root for the puffin to catch the very same fish that we were rooting for the previous week, without a single thought for whether or not that poor little fish has managed to complete its reproductive cycle in time before becoming dinner. "Yes," she said, "one of life's great paradoxes!"

The woman also explained to me how the actions of human beings were the principal reason that the snow leopard is now an endangered species, and the difference adopting one could make to the future of this magnificent animal. She spoke with both compassion and authority, and I became very excited about this prospect and couldn't wait to get home that night and discuss it with Helen. Unfortunately, Helen, in her inimitable, level-headed, pragmatic way, made a very good point. "The idea sounds all well and good in theory," she said, "but where would we put the thing? We barely have room to swing a moggy in this place, let alone a snow leopard.* Maybe if we get a bigger house somewhere down the line, we can think about it again then."

* A snow leopard may be out of the question, but for Helen and me, a pet completes a family, and the Buckleys are big dog lovers.

I did feel sorry for the poor assistant in the pet shop where we got Snoopie, our Golden Retriever. A man walked up to the counter and, in a soft, muffled voice, said, "Hello, I'd like to buy a wasp."

The assistant could barely make out what the man was saying and answered, "Sorry, Sir, I didn't quite catch that."

In the same muffled voice, the man repeated, "I'd like to buy a wasp." "Very sorry, Sir," the assistant said. "My hearing isn't up to much today. Could you say that a little louder?"

"I'd like to buy a wasp."

Still not sure that he'd heard correctly, the assistant hesitantly asked, "You'd like to buy a wasp?"

"Yes, please."

"Sorry, Sir," the assistant replied, "but we don't sell wasps."

Confused, the man said, "Oh, it's just that I walked past the shop the other day, and I saw one in the window."

I love this amusing story of the accidental heroine from Cornwall, as recounted to me by her daughter Faye. Not prepared to allow her besetting health problems to triumph, her mother would battle through the challenges of each day with dignity, resolve and a smile. However, over time, this proud woman's mobility deteriorated until she was barely able to walk twenty yards unassisted. In an attempt to help restore their mother's independence, Faye and her two sisters, Louise and Lorraine, clubbed together and bought her a brand-new, gleaming red mobility scooter. Everyone in the village was keen for her to use it and become active again in the community, but for the first year or so, it sat in the garage gathering dust. Despite gentle encouragements every so often from the girls, she'd always say, "No, I've never driven before. Your dad took me everywhere, and I don't feel confident on the roads." In truth, Sylvia had always been a very private person shying away from the limelight and, silly though she knew it was, felt very self-conscious about riding her electric scooter in public.

One warm summer's afternoon, however, whilst everyone was out, fed up with being confined to the house, she plucked up the courage to give it a go. After a little practice in the backyard, she decided to bite the bullet and hesitantly pulled out of the gate, turned right onto the lane and began heading down to the general store to get a pint of milk, loaf of bread and her paper. Thirty seconds or so along the road, from behind her, she could suddenly hear the sound of laughter, cheering and music. When she turned her head to see what all the commotion was about, to her complete terror, a big brass band, baton twirlers, floats and a mass of merrymakers were moving in on her. How could she have forgotten that it was carnival day! Trapped and panic-stricken, this poor, terrified lady did the only thing she could do in the circumstances – styled it out! To great cheers of "Go, Sylv," with a smile and a wave, she heralded the procession the last few hundred yards onto the village green and has been a permanent fixture ever since.

Of all the incredible people I have encountered, the one that inspired me the most is, without doubt, the elderly gentleman that had conquered major personal adversity to lead an amazing, almost Indiana Jones-like lifestyle.

I picked him up from King's Cross Station* to take him to Waterloo Station for a connecting train down to Dorset. He was wearing one of those khaki safari suits with the shorts, open-toe sandals and *Crocodile Dundee*-style hat, and donned a big, bushy white beard (like he'd just eaten a nice, whole, juicy sheep for lunch – yum, yum!) and could just about see through his thick bottle lens glasses. As I was putting his large metal-framed rucksack in the boot, I was struck by the array of stickers that adorned it, presumably from many of the places around the globe that he had ventured – Papua New Guinea, Beirut, the Andes, Cambodia, Chad, Haiti, Benin, Togo, Burnham-on-Crouch, Newport Pagnell and Basingstoke.

A very modest and self-effacing gentleman, he told me that for the past fifty years he had been an Australian peace envoy and humanitarian delegate, working on many major aid projects in some of the most troubled regions of the world. I asked him what his most memorable 'adventure' had been, and he recounted one expedition to the plains of the Serengeti, on which, during a freak monsoon, he had become detached from the rest of the party. Alone and facing almost certain starvation, all he had by way of provisions was a couple of Oxo cubes and a few root vegetables that he had gathered. With great effort, however, and the aid of a very crude spear that he had knocked up, he managed to hunt down a hyena and made himself a 'laughing stock', which sustained him until he was finally rescued by one of the guides three days later.

But do you know the most incredible thing about this amazing arthritis-ridden man who could barely see but a few feet in front of himself? He had wooden legs – and real feet!

* As I sat outside King's Cross Station waiting for my passenger to arrive, I thought back on some of the 'interesting' experiences I had had when I used to commute in and out of London by train each day. One that came to mind was travelling home on the Central Line one rush hour. As I was waiting for the train at Holborn Station, I couldn't help but notice three stunning young ladies on the platform chatting away. When the train arrives, as we're getting on, one of the girls turns to continue her conversation with her friends and starts backing up towards me. I turn round to face the other way, when suddenly, after a second or two, I feel this body docked up against me. Because of the sheer volume of people crammed in the carriage, I literally hit a wall and couldn't move an inch. In fact, it was so crowded that I had an itch in my right calf, and, as I eased down, I scratched the wrong leg! Anyway, I could feel the contours of the back against my back and the transfer of body heat – really lovely and sensual! For a moment, I was basking on a tropical island surrounded by scantily clad ladies in ra ra skirts! *No, this is wrong. This young lady is half your age. What are you thinking? Pull yourself together, man, you've been happily married for the best part of ten years and you love Helen more than life itself.*

But then, you never caused this situation. You didn't manipulate it in any way. You're a victim of circumstances here. So, just shut up and enjoy it. Get stuck in a tunnel, be a signal failure, somebody faint, somebody pull the emergency alarm! (You would tell me if I am a bad man, wouldn't you?)

When we stopped at Chancery Lane, and a couple of people got off and the pressure was slightly relieved, I couldn't help but sneak a cheeky peek at her over my shoulder. To my total horror, the three stunning young ladies were standing about three feet to the side and this massive brute of a man in a pinstripe suit, the spitting image of Popeye's adversary, Bluto, with big, bushy black beard and eyebrows, was welded up against me!

YUCK, YUCK, YUCK. HELP, GET ME OUT OF HERE!

Totally ashamed of myself, and fearing that Helen would somehow be able to read my mind the second I walked through the door, I rushed home at breakneck speed, bolted straight up to the shower and scrubbed my skin red raw. I then changed, splashed on a bit of Paco Rabanne and casually went down to the living room like everything was perfectly normal, and smothered Helen with kisses and cuddles for the next five minutes.

"What have you been up to now, Buck, my lad?"

"Nothing, my sweet. Can't the luckiest husband in the world give his amazing, beautiful, sexy wife a little affection just because? I'll do the dishwasher tonight, baby. And why don't you just kick back, relax and catch up on your soaps this evening? You deserve a break from time to time too, you know! Let me arrange those cushions for you so you can get yourself all lovely and comfy-cosy. Now isn't that better, eh? Kiss, kiss. And I'll bring you a nice cup of tea and some of your favourite biscuits through later! Love you!"

I think I dealt with that 'little situation' surprisingly well under the circumstances, even if I do say so myself!

Left of centre

Personally, I love to meet people that don't fit neatly into boxes, the ones that both entertain us and challenge our world views.

One such person was a very pleasant, soft, well-spoken, late-middle-aged gentleman with just the slightest hint of a Wiltshire accent. As he sat quietly on the back seat working on his papers, he suddenly exclaimed, "Can someone please tell me the earthly point of these infernal silent letters in words?"

I wasn't quite sure whether this was a rhetorical statement, so I just replied, "Yeah, I know, they can be right little *dashingtons*." I sort of know what he means, though. I have thought similar myself in the past. They obviously have their origins somewhere in the evolution of our language, but, yes, on the surface, the spelling of words like *gnaw, knead* and *pterodactyl* do appear rather senseless. But, for me, it is these sorts of little oddities that make the English language so rich and interesting. Anyway, the next thing I knew he had his notepad out and was crunching away on his calculator for the following ten minutes or so before calling, I presume, his wife: "Hello, darling… Yes, just in a taxi on my way to the hotel... No, I had something earlier on the train... panini, chips, a nice slice of banoffee pie and a Coke... Once in a while isn't going to hurt me... Okay, I'll be extra good when I get home, promise... No, I will probably just have a quick shower and fall straight into bed so that I am nice and fresh for the morning... Will do, yes, of course. Darling, I've just had an epiphany... yes, yes, very amusing, but, darling, listen, this is serious. Silent letters in words. I've been doing a few calculations, very crude at this stage, you'll understand, but I've worked out that the average person of three score years and ten wastes, wait for it, between six and nine hours of their life writing or typing silent letters. Precisely, no difference at all. We'd still know exactly what the word meant without them... That's exactly what I thought. Given the choice, who's going to say, 'Oh, yes, I'd like to spend six, seven, eight, nine – whatever – hours of my life writing silent letters, please'? Well, yes, apart from Timothy, that is. No, life is far too precious for that... but sadly, darling, I fear it is probably a little too late for us. The curse of the silent letter has struck and already robbed us of some five and a half hours of our time on this earth that we can never get back. But what about Tarquin and Astra and the grandchildren, and their children, and their children to come? I agree, we need to start a campaign straight away, without delay, to challenge the conventional literary wisdom and get these pointless silent letters banished from our language once and for all and prevent future generations from falling prey to them... Yes, I'll be home first thing Saturday morning and we'll get straight on it...That would be wonderful, darling, and, in the meantime, I think we need Eugene and Clare on this one. So, if you wouldn't mind appraising them in my absence, that would help speed things up immensely... I will

43

do, darling, love you too, bye-bye [*kiss, kiss*]… And, darling, don't forget to change the litter tray… [*click*] Oh, she's gone."

Totally bonkers – but we need more totally bonkers!

A few people I have encountered along the way, however, push the envelope of eccentricity beyond acceptable limits.

A couple of summers back, I collected an investment banker from Canary Wharf, Docklands – a very attractive, elegant, well-spoken businesswoman in her late thirties/early forties. (A little bit on the dumpy side, but that's neither here nor there!) She was carrying an expensive-looking lady's leather briefcase and a number of large lever arch files, so I got out, opened the back door and helped her with her things. I then asked her if she preferred the windows open or the air conditioning on, and whether she would like to listen to a little music on the way. She thanked me and told me that I was a gentleman, and then immediately proceeded to nibble on her nails. This may well have been the result of executive stress, or just a habit that she had developed over the years, I don't know, but, in any case, I don't think it is very ladylike for a woman to bite her toenails in public!

And then there was the 'twilight zone' episode with the woman in her eighties* with the lovely jolly round face, blue rinse, hairnet and coat with fur collar. I asked her if she would like to listen to a little radio. I thought she might appreciate some easy listening, a little bit of Radio 2 or Classic FM, or maybe a Radio 4 play. She said, "That's very kind of you, dear, but I have my own music with me," and promptly proceeded to place a whacking great pair of Beats on her head. As I looked back in the rear-view mirror, I could see her head rocking away. After five minutes or so, her mobile went off and she pulled her headphones down around her neck. The volume was up on max and with some real heavy grime blaring out. She answered:

"Yo, Mavis, whazup, girl?… You gotta tell your Reggie to get down dat doctor's and sort out his little ting, ya know what I'm saying, girlfriend?… I've told my Stan he's taking me to see dat new *Transformers* movie at da weekend. And he'd better be splashing da Ps."

Come on, who hasn't got a little bit of *street* in them!

* This reminds me of the story I heard about another spunky old dear years ago on the radio. She loved her Galaxy Smooth milk chocolate bar, and would indulge herself on the train home from Wilmslow, Cheshire to Chiswick, West London, after her monthly visit to her sister Alice. On this particular occasion, as had been her routine every month or so for the past thirty-odd years, she stopped off at the little kiosk in the station to purchase her treat:

"Hello, Molly, leaving us so soon?"

"Afraid so, George, I've got a WI meeting in the morning. Princess Camilla, Duchess of Cornwall, is attending, and I've made some lovely raspberry jam especially for the occasion."

"Sounds lovely. I might pop along myself."

"You'd be very welcome."

"Your usual delight for the journey, I presume."

"But of course."

"Have a safe trip home, my love, and behave yourself."

"Where's the fun in that?"

"That's the spirit, girl!"

Halfway along the line, a young goth – all in black with his ghoulish motifs and accessories, dyed black hair, piercings, colourful contact lenses and fake fangs – that had been sitting opposite her for the past four or five stops, picked up the Galaxy Smooth from the table, broke off a square, popped it in his mouth and put the bar back down on the table.

Ooh, the cheeky monkey.

Molly then picked up the chocolate, broke off a square, popped it in her mouth and placed it back down on the table.

The goth gave her a strange look. A few seconds later, he picked up the bar again, broke off another square, which he proceeded to consume, and placed it back on the table.

Why, the insolent little... I've got a good mind to...

Molly again picked up the bar, broke off a square, began eating it and placed the bar back down.

With only one square remaining, a Mexican standoff ensued – the tension in the air was high, gazes alternating between the chocolate and the eyes, each waiting for the slightest twitch or sign of weakness in the other. Finally, the goth makes his move, but Molly is too quick for him. She lunges forward and grabs the wrapper a fraction of a second ahead of the goth. To the goth's dismay, slowly and gleefully, she directs her spoil towards her mouth and, with an expression of sheer bliss on her face, rolls it around her mouth, savouring every second, before the square disappears forever.

For the next half-hour or so until the dazed goth

reaches his stop, Molly glances up periodically from her macramé lacing only to snarl and grimace at the defeated party opposite. *This young reprobate will certainly think twice before trying it on with the next 'poor, frail, helpless little old biddy'*, she chuckles to herself.

When she finally arrived home, Molly reached into her handbag for her front door key, and pulled out the Galaxy Smooth milk chocolate bar that she had purchased earlier in the day from George at the little station kiosk in Wilmslow, Cheshire.

"Oh dear!"

On the subject of our senior members, I once had the immense honour and privilege of picking up the oldest person in the world from Gatwick Airport, Mr Li Wei Wok, from the Shandong region of East China, and taking him and his parents down to the Barbican Arts and Conference Centre where he was conducting a seminar on the secrets to a long and happy life. Lovely, lovely family (and he didn't look a day over 110!).

But, for me, there is one group of 'odd bods' that I just do not get – people who contact radio stations for a mention or dedication!

I'm not talking about people requesting a mention or dedication for somebody else, like this lady:

"Hi, Lynn, really love the show. Next Thursday will be our golden wedding anniversary. Could you please tell my Earnest that he is the most wonderful man in the world and I love him more and more with each passing day? And would you kindly play a song that has very special meaning for us both, and has seen us through the good and the 'challenging' times together over the past fifty years – *Knees up Mother Brown*."

That's absolutely fine, nothing wrong with that at all. No, I'm referring here to people that ask for a mention for themselves – why, oh why, oh why?

"Hi, Lynn, great show as usual. Just chilling on the couch after a long week at work – prosecco in hand and moggy, Simba, on lap. Would appreciate a mention. Stella."

"Hi, Stella, lovely to hear from you as always. We've got another hour of fantastic mellow music lined up, so just kick back and relax. I'll join you for a glass later. In the meantime, give Simba a big tickle under the chin from me. Here's Whitney... saving all her love... just for you!"

=

One happy Stella!
No, sorry, do not get it!
To all the Stellas out there, unscramble this:

You to a ! get do need really life

We're what we do, not what we say we're gonna do!

Or, as Groucho Marx so succinctly put it:

'*Sincerity is the key to success. Once you can fake that you've got it made*'.

As we journey through life, we meet people that we really like, those that we can take or leave, and some that we really don't care that much for at all! That's just natural. But for me, the one quality, above any other, that determines the level of respect that a person commands from me, is – do their actions match their words?

Take my Uncle Brian (twice removed, three times evicted), for instance, who is probably the stingiest person I have ever known. He made his fortune in fruit and veg, but a pound note is his governor! When, for example, an advert comes on the television requesting a small donation for a needy charitable cause, it'll be, "You know me, mate. I would if I could." Then, on a Saturday evening as he's waiting for the lottery results, he'll come out with, "If I won five million pounds on the lottery, I'd keep two million for myself and live off the interest, and give the rest to charity!"

In terms of passengers coming up short in the 'genuineness' stakes, three in particular stick out in my mind.

The first was a man by the name of Dr James Blackwood. He informed me that he was a leading educationalist that traversed the globe training and advising governments on the latest in educational innovation. He made a big issue of playing down his doctorate, which he insisted, 'isn't worth the paper it's written on', and never used the title Doctor, because, as a proud working-class lad from a council estate in Preston, Lancs, he didn't like the way it made him sound pretentious. About twenty minutes into the journey, his mobile rang. Upon answering, his voice lowered to a deep, rich, velvety tone – "Dr James Blackwood speaking. How can I help?"

The second example was the breathtakingly stunning young woman I took from her Chelsea apartment to a West End nightclub. Her heavily made-up face was flawless and her figure Barbie Doll-perfect, leaving little to the imagination. It didn't surprise me to learn that she starred in a well-known reality TV show. She told me how she absolutely deplored the degrading sexual objectification of beautiful women to promote products, as this led to false and unrealistic expectations, especially in young girls, that could lead to serious feelings of inadequacy and depression. When we arrived at the club and the rear door was opened for her, she puckered up, put a sultry expression on her face, slivered sexily out of the car and walked bolt upright with her ample bosom pushed out and head slightly tilted back, pursued by a swarm of frenzied paparazzi snapping away at her!

What reaction does this third scenario elicit within you?

I picked up a top executive from a big petro-chemical corporation in the City and took him to Leatherhead Station in Surrey to pick up his car for his onward journey to his home about five miles out. He was a pleasant man and we exchanged a little chit-chat along the way. When he asked me about my working patterns, I told him that I generally do around twelve hours a day, Monday to Friday, to which he replied, "If you will allow me, my friend, and trust me, I speak from personal experience, money will never bring you true happiness." He then proceeded to share with me how he had once been completely driven by the pursuit of wealth and success – which had almost cost him his marriage and had induced a near-fatal heart attack in the process. Following a triple by-pass and feeling at an all-time low, however, as he was waiting in the hospital transport lounge for his cab home, a 'chance' encounter with a Far Eastern hospital porter at the vending machine embarked him on a journey to enlightenment and inner contentment, in which materialism has no place. His whole being has now realigned as he walks the path set for him by the universe. His eyes have been opened and, now, for the first time in his sixty-two years on this earth, he appreciates the real beauty in life, the simple things that we all take for granted – the laughter of his grandchildren at play, the smell of a scented flower, a phone call with an old friend.

As he spoke, his words resonated deep within me. My life certainly felt turbulent and disjointed. The times that I have shouted out to the kids to shut up when they were innocently at play, just because I was totally exhausted and had to get up at 5 am the next day for an airport run! Or the occasion that Helen excitedly called me into the garden one warm summer's day to smell the scent of the lavender in bloom that she had planted the year before, and I said that I'd be out after the football, but fell asleep! Or the number of times I've meant to check in with an old buddy, but life just got in the way!

Sure, I was working sixty hours plus a week to keep the wolf from the door as well as putting in the odd Saturday when we had a big bill to pay or Christmas was approaching. Like any husband and father, I wanted to provide the best I could for my family and try to give my children the opportunities I never had, and to make sure we at least got a week away somewhere each year, which generally meant a Hoseasons holiday park in Dorset. But, in so doing, how many things had I missed out on in my family's life? Special moments that I can never reclaim, like the children's sports days and Christmas concerts, and Helen's graduation from her beaded jewellery-making class.

As we talked, I began listing ways in my mind of making economies so that I could afford to take the odd day off from time to time and create some cherished memories with my family and friends:

- Sourcing the best savings accounts for the little bit we had managed to stash away for a rainy day.
- Checking out the most competitive energy deals on Uswitch.
- Purchasing supermarket own brands rather than the named brands, especially as many argue that there is generally very little difference in quality anyway.*
- Going to the nearest petrol station when I am out on the road, rather than driving miles out of my way to find a Shell garage so that I can add a few extra pence onto my Shell Go+ card. (Intellectually, I know that this is a false economy, but the seductive allure of those loyalty reward points racking up with each visit to the pump is virtually impossible to resist!)
- Changing my snooker night with my old workmate Barry – in which I generally spend around £15 – from fortnightly to four-weekly, thus achieving an instant annual saving of £195.
- Persuading Helen that she could look just as lovely in clothes from a budget store or charity shop simply by accessorising with the right costume jewellery, scarves, belts, etc.
- Convincing the kids that a day out in the countryside exploring the forests and wading through streams, etc., is just as much fun as going

to a theme park. And, with the right fillings, I'm sure they will find homemade sandwiches just as tasty as a McDonalds!

I felt quite pleased with myself with the potential savings I was able to conjure up just off the top of my head and, with Helen's help, was sure there were more to be found.

As we neared our destination, I thanked the man for his insight and illumination. I felt uplifted, confident that re-evaluation of my priorities would yield serious benefits for both my family and myself!

When we finally arrived at Leatherhead Station, he directed me towards the end of the car park and told me that his car was the Bentley in the far left-hand corner!

Yes, I think it is probably much the same reaction as that elicited within me!

---

* With one notable exception, that is: toilet roll! It may seem like money down the pan, but, for me, this is the one product that I will never scrimp on. The old 'Farmer Giles' aside, I think my doggedness when it comes to good-quality quilted paper probably stems from being at school during the age of the 'tracing paper' toilet roll and knowing, first-hand, the deep, long-term effects this can have on a person!
Note: Cushelle Original is my personal tissue of choice – its 2-ply cushioned design, with its cleverly engineered micro air pockets, ensures softness and absorption for a comfortable, clean feeling every time.

This encounter brought to mind these words of wisdom imparted to me by my dear old mum when I was a young man just starting out on my own. "Son," she said, "let me give you a little word of advice. Money doesn't bring you happiness. But it's better to be rich and miserable than poor and miserable!"

And, have you ever noticed what a bizarre phenomenon debt management can be? If, for example, you're, say, ten thousand pounds in debt, and your child asks you if you will take them to Disneyland for their birthday, you will probably sit them down and lovingly explain that it is not possible right now, but you promise to take them just as soon as you can, and you'll all have a wonderful time. If, however, you are half a million pounds in debt and your child asks you if you will take them to Disneyland for their birthday, it's like, "Yeah, why not!"

The best in the business!

Occasionally, in the course of my work, I have the very real privilege of meeting some of the sharpest minds in their respective fields. Of these, three have been particularly noteworthy.

The first was an eminent psychologist, Professor Hugo McFarlane. He was a very distinguished-looking man in his mid-sixties who spoke with a soft, well-placed Edinburgh accent. He wore a tweed jacket with leather arm pads, brown corduroy trousers, brown suede brogues and deerstalker hat, and sported a grey Musketeer-type beard and moustache. He had just attended an international diversity conference where he had been the keynote speaker in his particular area of expertise, that of gender equality.*
This guy was old school, a straight talker and, I must say,

surprisingly non-PC. He said that he would probably get hung, drawn and quartered these days for saying this, but, "There are differences between men and women!" According to him, for example, men have naturally better spatial ability than women, which explains why there are still fewer women in tertiary education studying science, technology, engineering and maths – all subjects where spatial ability is essential. When it comes to the cognitive faculty of memory, however, he asserted that a woman's power of recall is far superior to that of a man.

I think he probably would get hung, drawn and quartered if he'd expressed these views in the earshot of my passenger, Rachel, an Adult Education College art tutor and active women's equality campaigner. She was explaining to me that there are minimal real defining differences between the sexes, with very few 'traditionally male' jobs or roles that women cannot perform equally as well, given the opportunity, and vice versa. She also informed me that, 'shock, horror', a woman's sex drive is just as high as that of a man. (I wish someone would tell that to Helen!) Women and men, therefore, 'should be treated no differently to each other'. A little later in the conversation, she shared with me that she had recently split up with her long-term boyfriend of seven years, and now, back on the scene, was taken aback at just how much dating convention had changed in this relatively short space of time, most notably, "When did guys suddenly think it attractive to start going Dutch on dinner dates?" One even had the audacity to ask her to pay the full bill because he thought she probably earned more than him!

Personally, I wouldn't pretend to be an expert in diversity, but I know exactly what the professor meant about women having a superior memory to men. Whenever I have a flaming row with Helen, the following day I can barely remember a thing, but she can recount every single detail word for word. In fact, so efficient is her memory that she can remember things that I didn't even say!

---

* For the record, can I state, clearly and unequivocally, that I personally have never discriminated between men and the fairer sex, and you can ask my better half if you don't believe me.

And, guys, we think we're the business when we whip out the old cordless drill, but have you ever tried to follow a knitting pattern?

13th Row: P1 [0:1:0:1:0],(k1, p1) 6 [9:11:14:16:19] times, p2, k8, * p2, C2B, p2, T3F, p3, C4F, p4, C4F, p3, T3B, p2, C2F, p2, * k8, p2, (p1, k1) 6 [9:11:14:16:19] times, p1 [0:1:0:1:0]

Respect!

This whole subject of gender equality calls to mind an ancient philosophical conundrum:

'If a man speaks in a forest and there is no woman around to hear him, is he still wrong?'

The second sharp mind of note was Professor Wyatt Levinson of Durham University, a pioneer in the comparatively new discipline of Mathematical Sociology, which as he explained to me is the area of Sociology that uses mathematics to construct social theories, providing a clarity and formality to the principally intuitive basis of sociological theory. I asked him what he considered his greatest achievement in his work.

"Greatest achievement? Um, that's an interesting question. Greatest achievement? Um, an interesting question indeed. Greatest achievement? What is my greatest achievement? Um, if pressed, I suppose I would probably say that my greatest achievement has to be the universal discovery that there are only three kinds of people in this world – those that can count and those that can't!"

The third was a young Chinese man, Jason Fong, a pioneer in Artificial Intelligence and chief executive of one of the world's most innovative and progressive new technology corporations. He was one of those fascinating characters that manage to seamlessly combine nerdism with exceptional business acumen and cool. He told me that, at the current rate of AI advancement, within my lifetime, robots will become indistinguishable from humans in virtually every aspect. It will even be possible to design your own ideal woman – her shape and size, the colour of her hair, her eyes, her skin complexion, even her personality and emotions. That night, I lay awake until the early hours of the morning, our conversation revolving over and over in my mind. I pondered the moral, ethical, cultural and spiritual implications of such a paradigm shift on the future of mankind as we know it and, in particular, the realisation that we may very soon be able to create the 'perfect' woman to order. Following great deliberation and soul-searching of this very profound prospect, I've reached my conclusion – I want one!

The age of celebrity

When people find out that I'm a London minicab driver, the first thing they ask me is invariably, "Do you ever pick up anyone famous?" Well, yes, I do. Just off the top of my head, you've got the immaculate Dr Hilary,* renowned ballet dancer and TV personality Wayne Sleep, busty Nurse Gladys Emmanuel from Open All Hours fame played by the ever-delectable Lynda Baron, and the actress, *Loose Women* star and national treasure that is Linda Robson. I've also picked up a number of cast members of *TOWIE* and *Love Island* (most notably, Kem, winner of the 2017 series). I don't know if that counts.

> * I was telling a painter and decorator mate of mine, Wozzle, down the Fatling in Hornchurch, what a genuinely nice person the heartthrob TV medic Dr Hilary was, from whence came the reply, "Never heard of her."

There is one celebrity encounter that I shan't be forgetting anytime soon! I was booked to pick up a passenger in the name simply of 'May'. When the person emerged from his house, I recognised him instantly, even though he wasn't quite as tall as I had imagined and looked a little 'portlier' than I recalled. He also had medium-length, wavy grey hair, rather than his trademark long, curly Dulux Dog mop. I could hardly believe that this modern-day living legend was sitting in the back of my car. The electricity coming off the guy literally made the hairs on the back of my neck stand up on end. What impressed me most, though, was that this superstar appeared to be a genuinely nice guy. I tried to play it cool, of course, and pretend that I was nonplussed, but he could obviously see that I was totally awestruck and made a big effort to exchange pleasantries with me and put me at ease.

When we arrived at our destination, realising that opportunities like this come but once in a lifetime, I blew caution to the wind and asked him for his autograph. Unfortunately, neither of us had any paper on us. I just had a receipt pad in my glove compartment which I didn't think was fitting for someone of this stature. He could see that I was disappointed and, to my delight, suggested a selfie together on my mobile, which came out surprisingly well. As I was animatedly shaking his hand and thanking him, I said, "My eldest son and I are both massive Queen fans and have all your albums. And can I just take this opportunity to say how very sorry I am about Freddie. I know how much he meant to you guys. He was an original, an icon in the truest sense of the word, and is sorely missed by us all." I gave his hand an extra squeeze of condolence before letting him go on his way.

I couldn't wait to get home that evening and show Toby the photo. As I excitedly relayed my encounter to him, he said, "Dad, you idiot. That's James May from *Top Gear*." Whoops!

Of all the celebrities I have picked up, my favourite has got to be the intrepid action man himself, Mr Bear Grylls.* I collected him from his home and took him to Epping Forest in Essex (AKA Borneo Jungle) to film one of his *Born Survivor* episodes. What a genuine, down-to-earth guy! No airs, no graces, just a lovely, lovely, upbeat gentleman full of positivity (apart from a few choice comments about Ray

Mears!). He was telling me that his real name isn't actually Bear Grylls. That was the name one of the young producers stumbled upon on the very first episode of the much-loved show, which has just stuck and really defined him ever since. No, his real name is actually Bear Hutchinson.

* Have you ever pondered the scene when Bear Grylls returns home from one of his expeditions, having spent the past few weeks or so dining on worms, slugs, insects, snakes, rats, and anything else that tingles his tastebuds, opens the front door, drops his kit in the passage and calls out to his wife – "Hi, honey, I'm home. How about a little bit of sugar for your Big Bear?"

Before I leave this section, I would just like to quickly come back to Dr Hilary for a moment, if I may. One for the ladies:

'It is possible for a guy to be too good-looking.' Discuss.

Chapter Five

What's in a Name?

Continuing on the subject of names, a name is a very powerful phenomenon that can have major implications for its owner. In fact, I would go so far as to say that a name can even determine a person's personality. Is it any coincidence that all Alfies from the age of three to twelve (and often beyond) are right little tykes?

So, choose your child's moniker wisely!

Name selection is obviously a very personal and subjective matter. That said, many parents don't appear to think things through too well before ascribing a potentially life-defining label to their child! I recently picked up a passenger displayed on my driver app as Campbell Angus. I naturally assumed that his name was Angus Campbell, as it is not uncommon for people to put their surname first on the booking. The soft-spoken young Scotsman told me that this was an almost daily occurrence, which had resulted in a number of awkward situations throughout his life, like this one in his GP's waiting room:

Receptionist: (*Calling out*) Angus Campbell, Mr Angus Campbell. Dr Masood will see you now in Room 2.

Campbell: (*Approaching receptionist*) Thank you, that's me, but I think you mean Campbell Angus.

Receptionist: No, it's Angus Campbell. (*Calling out again*) Mr Angus Campbell to see Dr Masood.

Campbell: It's an easy mistake to make, it happens to me all the time, but if you check your notes, you'll find it's actually Campbell Angus.

Receptionist: No, it's definitely Angus Campbell.

Campbell: (*Starting to get a little tetchy now*) After twenty-three years, I think I should know my own name by now, don't you?

Receptionist: Perhaps, but it's Angus Campbell.

Campbell: With respect, can I just say that I find your whole attitude really quite…

With this, an elderly gentleman shuffles over on his walking frame.

Elderly Gentleman: Sorry to hold you, lassie. Angus Campbell to see the doctor about my bunion.

Campbell: Oh!

Here's another head-scratcher. If your surname is Jones, and your son was born within the past fifty years, given the vast abundance of names at your disposal, what would be the one Christian name that you would definitely not give him? Exactly! Well, around the time they were filming the second series of *The Voice*, I got a job down to pick up 'Tom Jones' from the ITV studios on the South Bank. As you can imagine, I went over the car about a thousand times to make sure there wasn't a dust particle in sight, and checked my route over and over to ensure I wouldn't be taking any wrong turns. As I'm waiting, I'm working out in my head how I should play it. I've picked up many celebs in my time, but Tom Jones is in a whole different league. This guy is top of the tree. So, do I act nonplussed and just make the odd comment about the weather? Or do I say how pleased I am to meet him, and that my mum has all his albums and saw him live at The Talk of the Town in 1969? I also wanted to find out what he thought Elvis would have said about him seeing Priscilla! As the 10.30 pm pick-up time approached, my pulse began to race and I could feel myself getting that prickly heat sensation all over. Needless to say, however, my passenger wasn't Tom Jones, Tom Jones. The Tom Jones I had the very great privilege to meet was a young, friendly, intelligent trainee production manager (originally from Solihull but now living in Dalston) with, from what I could see, a very bright future ahead of him in the TV industry.

With all the young Tom Joneses, Andy Williamses and Michael Jacksons I have encountered, I guess it is only a matter of time before I pick up a young, fresh-faced Engelbert Humperdinck!

I should imagine that sharing a name with a well-known person is not without its issues. That said, what would be more problematic, having the same name as someone famous, or having a name very similar to that of someone famous? Examples of such names that have crossed my path include Lisa Stimpson, Dawn Trench, Annie McPhee,

Adrian Bole and Johnny Inglis. As excellent as each of these near-names are in their own right, there is one, I believe, that towers far above the rest and, dare I postulate, may well be unbeatable!

And that name is:

Wait for it…

Patience…

It will be worth the wait, trust me…

Sean Connelly

Didn't I tell you it would be worth the wait?

Chapter Six

You Can't Close Your Ears Off

The things that I overhear from my passengers afford me a unique and fascinating insight into their diverse worlds.

Making sense of the world!

Have you ever noticed that when you glance up at the clouds on a warm summer's day, you might see the shape of, say, a dog chasing a rabbit? Or, when you're staring at an everyday object, within its haphazard patterns and textures, you suddenly see a face. (Ken Barlow from *Coronation Street* has appeared frequently on my toast over the past few years!)

This is a psychological phenomenon, innate within us all, known as *pareidolia*, which predisposes our brains to extract meaning from random data. As well as the visual, this phenomenon also applies to auditory stimuli.

Bearing in mind that I cannot speak a word of foreign,

whilst listening to two young Nordic lovelies going at it hammer and tong in their own tongue (try saying that when you've had a few!) in the back of the car, in my brain's attempt to make sense of the nonsense jibber jabber entering my ears, these are some of the words I 'heard':

Paul Daniels; A finger of fudge is just enough to give the kids a treat; Come on, Eileen, too rye aye; He can shove his dashington engagement ring up his dashington dashington... but I still really dashington love the dashington; You're gonna like it, but not a lot; Barnacle Bill; Don't miss the DFS* Summer Sale – amazing discounts with up to fifty per cent off on selected items, but hurry, sale must end soon; and Debbie McGee.

* Given that DFS holds a sale for what must be forty-eight weeks of the year, what if you're the one who haplessly strolls into a store one Saturday afternoon and buys a settee on one of the other four weeks?

That cloak of invisibility I got for Christmas works a treat!

One thing that never ceases to astonish me, especially in this hypersensitive age of confidentiality and data protection in the workplace, is the things that people openly discuss in my presence the moment they get into the car – why so-and-so won't be getting their annual bonus this time round, who everyone hates behind the scenes on *Dancing on Ice*, what politician will be coming out of the closet next and the ones that keep getting caught in the closet. If I was so inclined, I could literally make a fortune off the tabloids!

It's as if I'm invisible, or don't have ears, or am a robot or something!

And some people are shameless to the point of insulting!

A few years back, I picked up a senior 'public servant' and his wife from a charitable event at the Guildhall, and drove them home to their country estate in Hampshire. The following conversation ensued:

All very light-hearted and playful.

Lord Oojamaflip: Very successful evening, I thought, darling, especially when Sir Hugh finally got his act together.

Lady Oojamaflip: Yes, it was, darling, and I can't believe we managed to exceed our target. The charities will be thrilled. Wonderful to see Giles and Arabella.

Lord Oojamaflip: As always, darling.

Lady Oojamaflip: I thought she looked absolutely stunning tonight, didn't you, darling? And she had it all on display with that plunging neckline.

Lord Oojamaflip: I can't really say that I noticed, darling.

Nudge in his ribs and both chuckle.

Lady Oojamaflip: Bunty has invited us over to the Chateau between Christmas and the New Year for a spot of skiing, darling.

Lord Oojamaflip: I'd go, darling, just to see them trying to prize old Humph into his salopettes.

Lady Oojamaflip: You can talk, darling.

She gives his tum a big rub.

Lord Oojamaflip: I don't know what you mean, darling. This is untrained muscle.

Mood change.

Lady Oojamaflip: It's such a shame you'll be in Thailand next week on your birthday, darling.

Lord Oojamaflip: Yes, I know, darling, but we can celebrate it together when I get back.

Lady Oojamaflip: I've always wanted to go to Thailand.

Lord Oojamaflip: The problem is, darling, this is public money, and I would find it very difficult to justify taking you along.

Lady Oojamaflip: But Henry is taking Felicity.

Lord Oojamaflip: That's slightly different, darling. Henry is a private contractor that works for us. You don't seem to grasp the difference between public and private funding.

Lady Oojamaflip: Of course I understand the difference between public and private funding. I'm not a fool.

Long awkward pause and blatant change of subject.

Lady Oojamaflip: I ordered the Christmas turkey in the week from the farm shop.

Another long uncomfortable pause.

Lord Oojamaflip: Are you suggesting, darling, that 'I' pay for you to come along?

Lady Oojamaflip: Well, yes!

Another slightly awkward pause. By now, I'm sitting there thinking – *The hotel room's already sorted so you won't have to fork out any extra for that, so, "Here you are, luv, I'm working all the hours under the sun to just about pay the bills and my taxes, but take my credit card and book yourself a flight!"*

Lord Oojamaflip: Leave it with me, darling. I think I may just be able to find an ambassadorial role for you.

Business mumbo jumbo

One thing that never ceases to make me smile is people desperately trying to peacock their corporate acumen with their 'business-speak' mastery. There is a place for this, I know, and, guys, even I can tell that you are incisive, can-do, big-picture operators. But the key is knowing when to turn it on and when to turn it off, unlike this elegant, early-middle-aged 'power couple', both executives at the same major investment bank in the City.

The man got into the car first and said that his wife would be out in a short while. He told me that she had flown back that afternoon from a Far Eastern business trip and had to head straight into an Executive Board debriefing. When she finally got into the car, he looked 'extremely pleased to see her' and gave her a lovely embrace:

(Please see Glossary of Jargon below.)

Executive woman: Hey, babe, missed you.
Executive man: Hey, babe, missed you more. How was the trip?

Executive woman:	Very eventful. I'll *gist* you over dinner this evening, but firstly, did you manage to book the annual leave?
Executive man:	Yes, finally got some *face time* with RJ. He wasn't exactly *bullish* about the timing, especially with the launch of the new 'Investment Strategy' reaching *critical mass*.
Executive woman:	*Bottom line* me?
Executive man:	Well, I've reassured him that I've done all the *heavy lifting* and have *full optics* on the project, and believe it is manageable for me to take the time off. He wants to *parachute* Lance Maybury *in* to oversee the final implementation in my absence.
Executive woman:	*LIHOM* Lance?
Executive man:	Yes, I know, but he's the only bod in this place with the *knowledge density* to cover for me for three weeks.
Executive woman:	The *bean counters* are not going to like it.
Executive man:	That's an understatement. But it's the least the organisation can do after *throwing me under a bus* in the spring and making me *punch the puppy*. And you, were you able to book the leave?
Executive woman:	Yes, I managed to get a brief *over-the-shoulder time* with Rupert after the debriefing. With all my other responsibilities, he was worried that I won't have the *bandwidth* to spearhead

	the China market. Stop looking at me like that!
Executive man:	What?
Executive woman:	You know exactly what!
Executive man:	So, did you lavish him with the requisite *ear candy*?
Executive woman:	Of course. I picked up the photograph on his desk and told him what a beautiful wife and children he has, and how fortunate they were to have him. Desist, you naughty man!
Executive man:	It's not my fault you're so irresistible. And I've been pining for you all week.
Executive woman:	That's as may be, *Mr Velvet Lip*, but if we're going to finally sort this vacation out, we need to really *double down*.
Executive man:	Sorry.
Executive woman:	I should think so!
Executive man:	Okay, I'm *laser-focused*. So, did he *rubber stamp* it?
Executive woman:	Yes, I've assured him that I will *front burner* Beijing. So, if I'm going to get my *ducks in a row* and be able to take the time off with a clear head, I'll be *paddling my canoe on both sides* for the next six weeks. Will you pack it up!
Executive man:	Sorry.
Executive woman:	Look, you're not *adding value* here.
Executive man:	Okay, *my bad*. Carry on.
Executive woman:	And, as an added measure to appease him, I've agreed to *triangulate* with Miranda the *Meanderthal*. I might be a

	week or so late arriving on the holiday while I wait for Miranda to get to the point.
Executive man:	Mean but true. So, now we just need to *align* on a destination. I think we've virtually scaled the globe with work alone. Do we need an *idea shower*?
Executive woman:	Well, I was thinking somewhere a little more far-flung. Personally, I'm quite *amped* by Mauritius.
Executive man:	Excellent choice. I can *buy in* on that.
Executive woman:	Right, that's enough. Sit on your hands!
Executive man:	But…
Executive woman:	No buts, sit on your hands. I need you to stop all this *tangentery* and *chasing butterflies* right this minute, because at the moment you're operating at *low-decision latitude*. That's better. So, as I was about to say, I've had a cursory glance at Mauritius.
Executive man:	Okay, *hum me a few bars*.
Executive woman:	Well, it looks like somewhere that we can *decompress* and spiritually reconnect. But, before we *book the goods*, we need to *peel the onion* and find out as much as we can about the place, especially the spa facilities.
Executive man:	No problem, I'll get one of my *desk jockeys* to take a *look under the bonnet*, and *ping* you by Wednesday next week.
Executive woman:	I mean it, Adam!

Executive man:	What? I'm just shifting position so I can face you better.
Executive woman:	Any more and I'll *cold towel* your 10 *o'clock*. Am I making myself *P A C*?
Executive man:	Bristol.
Executive woman:	Adam!
Executive man:	I meant, crystal.
Executive woman:	That's more like it. Right, now we've just got to *air out* the budget.
Executive man:	Well, we should be able to get a decent discount through the bank's travel agent with the volume of business we pass their way every year. And with our combined air miles, this one should virtually *wash its own face*.
Executive woman:	Great. So, once we get the information by the middle of next week, we'll let it *marinate* for a couple of days and *circle back* same time next Friday.
Executive man:	Okay, so I think we have *agreeance*. Can I take my hands out now?
Executive woman:	No!

GLOSSARY OF BUSINESS JARGON

JARGON WORD	DEFINITION
Added value	Anything that enhances value
Agreeance	Agreement
Air it out	To discuss an issue openly
Alignment	Consensus
Amped	Having a large amount of excitement and energy
Bandwidth	The physical and mental limit of your working ability
Bean counter	A derogatory term for an accountant
Book the goods	Place an order
Bottom line it	To summarise
Bullish	To be in favour of
Buy in	To agree with a particular position
Chasing butterflies	A state of distraction by those who are easily distracted
Circle back	To revisit an issue
Cold towel	To put on hold
Critical mass	The point reached by a new idea or product just prior to explosive market growth
Decompress	To release from pressure
Desk jockey	An office worker
Double down	To continue to do something in an even more determined way than before

Ducks in a row	To become organised
Ear candy	Flattery
Face time	The opportunity to sit down to discuss an issue in person
Front burner	The opposite of back burner and reserved for the most pressing matters
Full optics	A complete view
Gist	To provide a summary
Heavy lifting	The hard work
Hum a few bars	A request to provide a verbal summary
Idea shower	A creative group exercise where suggestions are made in rapid succession
Knowledge density	A vague measure of expertise
Laser-focused	To be so accurately centred on target that you can't miss
LIHOM	Legend In His/Her Own Mind
Look under the bonnet	Analyse a situation
Low-decision latitude	Inability to make any important choices
Marinate	To allow some time to consider an idea privately
Meanderthal	A person who has difficulty expressing themselves succinctly, and often gives long, unfocused presentations

My bad	Accept you are wrong or something is your fault
O'clock	Meeting at a specific time
Over-the-shoulder time	An informal training or review session conducted in person
PAC	Perfectly absolutely clear
Paddle on both sides	To apply the maximum effort to a task
Parachute in	To send someone to complete work at an off-site location
Peel the onion	To remove all superfluous layers and get to the heart of an issue
Ping	To contact or notify
Punch the puppy	To take an unpopular action
Rubber stamp	Approval
Tangentery	Distracting side topics
Throw under a bus	To betray an acquaintance to divert blame
Triangulate	To involve a third person or party
Value added	To contribute something extra
Velvet lip	Gift for smooth talking
Wash its own face	Pay for itself/break even

I'm sure they had a lovely evening together!

Word to the wise – consider carefully what you say in front of the driver:

Taking up the sub-theme of the above scenario, given the uncensored behaviour of some passengers in the back of the car, it would seem as if they think that we minicab drivers are completely naïve when it comes to things of the carnal. Well, believe it or not, we are flesh and blood with the same hormones coursing through our veins as everybody else, and I, for one, am quite savvy on the subject, thank you very much! So, if you prefer to arrive at your destination on time, without causing any unnecessary detours, you may wish to avoid distracting the driver by saying or doing anything of even a mildly erotic nature, and definitely no talk pertaining to homogenous regions!

In addition, not realising that drivers have ears, passengers may inadvertently offend them at their own peril.

An old patriotic colleague of mine, Kazimierz, was taking a group of Australian lads to Gatwick Airport to catch their plane home to Canberra. A little way down the road, one of the boys suddenly exclaims, "Guys, guys, question. What is another name for a London telephone box?"

"We don't know, mate. What is another name for a London telephone box?"

"A urinal."

Fits of hysterics! True as this may be, without saying a word, Kazi subtly deviated off and onto a highly congested route where they sat in a tonne of traffic for the next ten minutes. Fortunately for the panicked lads, who'd barely allowed sufficient time in the first place, after achieving his desired reaction, Kazi took a few back doubles to get the boys to the airport on time. Not all drivers, however, may have been so excusing!

Chapter Seven

Shooting the Breeze

For me, the most enjoyable aspect of my work has to be the interactions with passengers. Following the customary "Hi, Driver, busy this evening?", "What time d'ya start?", "What time ya finishing?", we mostly chat about ordinary everyday things, as you would expect. Sometimes, however, conversations can take some interesting detours.

Every day's a school day
With all the fascinating little factlets that passengers have passed my way over the years, my kids reckon I should go on *Tipping Point*!

Did you know, for instance, that:

    a.   London is divided up into four main postcodes: N for North London, E for East London, W for West London, but something I'd never clocked before, no S for South London, only SE (South East) and

SW (South West). The S postcode actually represents Sheffield. (*Imran, Royal Mail Sorting Office.*)

b. Jimmy Hendrix wrote his trademark hit, *Purple Haze*, at the Upper Cut Club in Forest Gate, London, E7. (*Lennox, local resident, big fan, and just had his third guitar lesson.*)

c. Women's obsession with wearing nice shoes is to impress other women and not the guys. (*Siobhan, Deputy Editor, Elle Magazine.*)

Whilst some people can be very guarded with their knowledge, there are those whose unbridled enthusiasm for sharing absolutely everything they know on a particular subject (regardless of the level of interest of the recipient) can give many a National Trust steward* a run for their money!

From my experience, the area in which people are the keenest to impart their knowledge is holidays. Whenever I receive holiday advice, I take it home to Helen, who then decides whether or not we will incorporate it into our travel plans. The problem, however, arises with passengers that I pick up on a regular basis. There have been a couple of times when Helen has meticulously planned a very tight schedule, and, to her frustration, knowing that they will quiz me upon our return, I have insisted on shoehorning a recommendation in, often at the cost of something she really wanted to do – "But, Helen, my darling, you don't understand. They were so excited and said that we absolutely have to do this and would regret it if we didn't. I know it'll be tight, but let's just try, eh, for me? You know I love you, sweetheart. You're the best!"

An example of this was the young 'Jack the Lad' investment banker I often drive home late at night from

Canary Wharf. When I told him that we were off to the Costa del Sol in a couple of weeks, he told me that he had an apartment out there, and that we definitely had to check out 'Laughlins' Irish Bar, and tell the manager, Sheamus, that we were friends of 'Wilko', and he would look after us. "I'm there five or six times a year and they absolutely love me at that place. Ask him to tell you what happened last September. Caused a bit of excitement, you might say! Geed 'em all up a bit!" I felt both obliged and intrigued, so, cutting our excursion to Porta Buenos short, we finally found Laughlins, out in the middle of nowhere, and, as instructed, introduced ourselves to Sheamus.

"Yes, I know Wilko, that *dashington* banker idiot. An absolute *dashington* nuisance. A *dashington* pain in the *dashington*. I wish he'd find somewhere else to go and *dashington* annoy... I don't remember any *dashington* incident last September."

As predicted, Wilko couldn't wait to hear about our visit to Laughlins, and what Sheamus had had to say about him.

"Yeah, you're definitely one of their more memorable customers, man."

Broad smile.

"Sheamus wouldn't tell us about the incident last year, though. Said he'd have to kill us if he did."

"That sounds like Sheamus, all right. My secret's safe for now, at least."

Even broader smile.

* Anyone that has ever visited a National Trust establishment will know exactly what I am talking about here. As an illustration, whilst looking around a stately home in Kent, I thought I'd better at least try and appear a bit interested as Helen's mum and dad had kindly bought us an annual membership for Christmas. So, as Helen and the kids were busy taking in every detail, I stopped to look at a painting on the wall of the home's garden. Within seconds, a woman's head appeared over my right shoulder.

"Beautiful, isn't it?"

"Yeah, yeah, lovely."

"It's a scene of the small private garden just before the Orangery. (*What's an orangery when it's at home?*) It was painted by Lady Blanchard herself, as are many of the paintings around the Home."

"Oh, really?"

"Yes. She had the most exquisite touch with a paintbrush. You can feel the emotion and intensity in every stroke. That's Lady Blanchard herself sitting on the white bench under the apple blossom tree."

"Is it really?"

"Yes, and if you look closely to the left, you can see the head of a little tabby cat poking out through the grass."

"Oh yeah, in the corner there."

"That was Mr Tibbli Doos II, her stalwart, her closest companion and confidant, especially during the extended times of the Lord Admiral's many overseas deployments. She would not go anywhere without Mr Tibbli Doos II by her side."

"I'm sure her husband had something to say about that."

"Well, as far as Lady Blanchard was concerned, The Lord Admiral and Mr Tibbli Doos II were the very best of friends. One big happy family, you might say. Privately, though, the two of them couldn't stand the sight of each other. I mean big time! On one occasion, whilst Lady Blanchard was in her boudoir powdering her nose before afternoon tea, the maid was reported to have seen the Lord Admiral holding Mr Tibbli Doos II up to his face by the scruff of the neck and saying, 'Now listen here, Doos, you mangy *dashington* fleabag. Any more smug sideways glances over at me when you're having a stroke on Cecily's lap, and your head is getting another dunking down the pan. Get it?'

"When Lady Blanchard entered the room, the Lord Admiral started cuddling and stroking Mr Tibbli Doos II and it was all, 'Who's a cute little kitty then, eh?' Mind you, Mr Tibbli Doos II could give as good as he got. For example, the Lord Admiral had a ritual of placing his biscuits on his saucer on his side table in his study and, whilst reading, would reach for one. On more than one occasion, Mr Tibbli Doos II would sneak up and slip a riga morticed mouse onto the saucer, which the Lord Admiral would proceed to dunk in his tea."

"That's fascinating."

"Yes, and Lady Blanchard was also a remarkable poet."

"Was she really?"

"Indeed. Her contemporary and close personal friend William Wordsworth once wrote of her – 'A profoundly gifted wordsmith with the common touch'. When you go up the stairs to her study, you'll see an anthology of her compositions on her bureau. You'll find my personal favourite on page 12. She penned this for her cousin, Lord Cholomondelley of Gloshem, who was going through a difficult spell of marital discord at the time. If I may, it goes:

'There was a man from Gloshem,
Who took off his clothes to wash 'em,
His wife said, Jack,
If you don't put 'em back,
I'll chuck 'em in the dustbin,
How about that?'"

"She sounds like an incredible woman."

"She certainly was. Ahead of her time in so many ways. And she received so much of her creative inspiration sitting on that very bench under the apple blossom tree with Mr Tibbli Doos II never far away."

"Actually, come to mention it, I remember seeing a woman dressed up in old-fashioned clothing, like in the picture, sitting on the bench with a tabby cat when we were walking through the grounds earlier. That's a great touch, really authentic. It gave me a little tingle at the time."

"Oh no, Sir, that wasn't a woman in costume. You are one of the many visitors over the years that have reported seeing the ghosts of Lady Blanchard and Mr Tibbli Doos II in the garden."

"Well, it has been lovely chatting. Thank you for all your time and keep up the good work."

"You're very welcome, Sir. Enjoy the rest of your visit."

"Psss, Helen, quick, come over here a minute."

"What?"

"You know when we were walking through the grounds on the way to the house, and we came to that lovely little garden with the white bench under the blossom tree?"

"Just by the Orangery?"

"Yeah. [*How does she know what an orangery is?*] Well, do you remember seeing a woman dressed up in old-fashioned clothes sitting on the bench with a cat?"

"No, there wasn't anybody on the bench when we walked by."

"Are you sure? Are you absolutely one hundred per cent sure?"

"Positive, because I was thinking of having a sit-down on it myself before Mathias ran off."

"Right, Helen, kids, we're off. No 'but Dads'. Come on, just hurry up."

Vroooooooooom!

What do you think of people who refer to plants by their Latin names?

~~Getting dragged around the Natio~~ Enjoying many a relaxed Sunday afternoon gently ambling around the stunning gardens of the National Trust with Helen, I find these are generally mother-and-daughter couples. The mother is in her early to mid-eighties and the daughter in her late fifties, early sixties. Both are immaculately turned out and speak assured Received Pronunciation (posh):

"Mother, come over here and look at this beautiful *Hemerocallis Lilioasphodelus*."

"Oh, Cynthia, it's splendid. That yellow would look absolutely divine interspersed with the pink of the *Nigritella Lithopolitanica* in my garden."

"A match made in Heaven, especially against the lavender backdrop of your *Gentianella Anisodonta*."

"All that's needed is a splash of red, perhaps *Gerbera Jamesonii*?"

"A magnificent festoon of colour!"

I know what I think!

In an attempt to help me 'chillax' by connecting more with nature, Helen has got me growing sunflowers. I was a bit sceptical at first, but I must say, it's actually very calming, and I've developed a real bond with every one of my twenty new 'besties', each with their own very distinctive characteristics. This probably sounds a bit whacky, I know, but I've even given them all individual names based on their resemblance to people I know. So, there's Nicola, Alfonso, seventeen Richards and Jess.

> And finally, on the subject of horticulture, like so many of the nation's defenceless middle-aged women who have fallen under his spell, Helen appears to have the real hots for the down-to-earth, everybody's-best-chum, butter-wouldn't-melt-in-his-mouth celebrity TV gardening legend, broadcaster, novelist and poet, Mr Alan Titchmarsh MBE. Have you any idea what that can do to a husband's self-esteem? If anybody ever says anything to me about it, I tell them straight and in no uncertain terms, "No, sorry, I'm afraid you're very much mistaken there. I think you'll find you actually mean George Clooney!"

One-way traffic

Occasionally, a passenger will appear open and chatty when they first get in, but it is not long into the 'conversation' that you realise the exchange is far from mutual, as in the case of Vera from Dagenham, Essex:

Vera: Just get me home, Driver. I'm shattered and need a nice cup of tea.

Me: Like that, is it?

Vera: I've had my grandson Alfie all day. It's half term at the moment. Ooh, he's such a little tyke, that one! He's only ten, but he's hyper intelligent and wears me out. And he's so good at maths.

Me: My ten-year-old's very good at maths.

Vera: They put him in the top set.

Me: Yeah, my boy's in the top set.

Vera: But the teacher said he gets bored easily. So, they've put him down, so he can help the slower kids. But he don't half take it out of me. It's not just that. Every time I go round there, I always end up having to tidy the place up as well. His wife's such a lazy cow.

Me: She is?

Vera: She does about sixty or seventy hours a week in one of those corporate law firm thingys, and is never around. My Gary has to do all the dinners when he gets home from work.

Me: I pick up a lot of people from the legal sector, and I know they're under incredible pressure and work ridiculous hours!

Vera: Selfish woman. She's from Surrey, and her family's got a few bob, know what I mean? They didn't want her to marry my Gary, because they didn't think we were good enough for their Jemima, oh no.

Me: That must have been difficult.

Vera: Even on the day of the wedding, her old man tried to pay my Gary off, but he wasn't having any of that.

Me: Good for him.

Vera: My Gary left school at fifteen and has slogged his guts out to build up his business.

Me: I started a business up once and I know how hard it is.

Vera: Nobody's ever handed anything to my Gary on a silver platter. That boy's had to graft for everything he's got.

Me: Something to be proud of.

Vera: He worked in that distilled water factory from the age of fifteen, and when it was going under, a few of them used their redundancy money and bought it out.

Me: That was brave.

Vera: And they've gone from strength to strength, and now they even supply right up in Berwick-upon-Tweed.

Me: You must be really proud of him.

Vera: And that lazy mare comes home at ten thirty every night – that's when she's not gallivanting off on some business trip somewhere or other for days on end – and can't even be bothered to do the washing. No, not that one, she has to send it out to… ooooh… 'Molly Maid'.

Me: Probably doesn't have the time.

Vera: I would never have dreamt of paying someone to do my washing. A woman should take care of the household.

Me: It's a different world these days.

Vera: Even when I worked three mornings a week in that bakery when my Gary was old enough to go to school, I would never have dreamt of sending my washing out. Never in a million years. Bone idle, that's what she is, bone *dashington* idle. Shameful woman!

Arrive at destination.

Me: Well, it's been nice chatting. Enjoy that cup of tea.

Vera: Yeah, bye.

Clunk.

The Encouragers

As well as the Veras of this world, I'm pleased to say that I also meet many people that seem genuinely interested in me and gladly impart words of advice and encouragement.*

I was chatting with one lovely lady about her kids' schooling, and happened to mention that I'd been asked to quizmaster a fundraising event for my Toby's Year 6 Residential to the Isle of Wight, but was wrestling with it, as I'd never done anything like that before. She reminded me that it was all for a good cause and that everyone would be on my side, as these occasions are more about having fun than a polished presentation. Encouraged by her words, I bit the bullet and agreed, and must say, thoroughly enjoyed the whole occasion.

The thing that shocked me the most was the amount of preparation that went into it. The most challenging aspect of the whole experience for me was probably coming up with the questions. Okay, no prizes, just for fun, see how you get on with the 'People' section. Answers in Appendix A at the end of the book.

1. How heavy was Gwen from Caerphilly when she was born on 2nd November 1976?

2. How heavy is Gwen from Caerphilly now?

3. Now a renowned entomologist, Lucy from Reigate, Surrey, first developed her fascination with insects at the tender age of nine when she befriended a daddy long legs in her father's allotment shed. Because of its distinctive gangly appearance and the slow, cumbersome way that it moved around, scattered with occasional bursts of frenetic energy, what name did she give to that spider?

4. Jagdeep from Hayes in Middlesex is a successful investment banker on a six-figure salary, but, at the age of five, what did he want to be when he grew up?

5. In 1969, to the delight of his parents, Rodric from Strathclyde was the first person in his family to pass his driving test. What was the make and model of his first car?

6. For a bonus point, what colour was that car?

As it was a family function, utilising my daughter, Charlotte's, artistic flair, I also designed this 'Spot the Difference' competition to help keep the youngsters occupied for a while. See how many differences you can spot between the two pictures.

Another source of real uplift to me was the fashion model I picked up from a Gucci shoot. From the way she spoke and her references to earls and baronesses, it came as no surprise to me to learn that this friendly, warm young lady was born into nobility. I was just astonished that, rather than talking about herself, she seemed genuinely more intrigued by my work and life. One thing she said that inspired me immensely was, "The aristocracy really admire the regular everyday people, you know. They have the greatest respect for their fortitude and the incredible way they manage to cope and just get on with life." What a lovely thing for her to say. I tell you, bolstered by these amazing sentiments, I felt like climbing up onto the nearest rooftop and shouting at the top of my voice for all to hear:

"Come on, world. Bring it on!"

* Encouragers are great people to be around. They emanate such positivity and make you feel like you can achieve anything you want to. I think this is probably one of the qualities that most attracts me to Helen. The night before the quiz, for example, I was lying in bed staring up at that ceiling, feeling really nervous and wondering what I'd let myself in for. I knew it was all only a bit of fun, but I really didn't want to do anything that would show the family, and especially Toby, up! Although I'd rehearsed what I was going to do multiple times, to really pull it off and get people in the spirit, I knew, needed a certain presence and charisma, which I was not confident I possessed. Helen turned over to me, gently stroked my cheek and said, "Hey,

sweetie, penny for your thoughts."
I said, "Oh, I'm just a little worried about the event tomorrow. What if they think I'm dull?"
She said, "Now you listen to me, Buck my lad. You can light up a room, simply by walking out of it."

It's good to get it off your chest

London is the greatest city in the world, bar none, fact! But that can come at a cost, with people stressed out and ranting and raving* about everything from litter everywhere, to spam calls, to the plight of the Lesser-Spotted Gobb Twit! One old boy, born and raised in Bethnal Green, a Londoner through and through and proud of it, told me in no uncertain terms that the reason he voted to leave the EU was because Europe was eroding our British identity and it was only a matter of time before they made Big Ben go digital!

Often, I can see where people are coming from, but there are times when I think to myself – is that really something worth flipping out over? Like the guy who had just said his farewells to a group of fellas and flung himself into the car, red with rage, exclaiming, "If another person calls me 'buddy', I swear, I'm gonna swing for 'em. I absolutely detest that expression." I sort of know what he means. It can come across as patronising, condescending, over-familiar, under-familiar, whatever. But like all these sorts of expressions – big guy, matie, chief, bro/bruv/cous, geezer, boss, cocker, chum, fella – it is generally used as a term of endearment and meant with the best of intentions. And there are certainly far bigger things to get yourself worked up about! As the old adage goes:

'Call me anything, but don't call me later for dinner.'

In fairness, I do struggle with pal and tosh, and, for me, 'mush' is the supreme insult and fighting talk where I come from!

So, is 'buddy' really worthy of a rant? Probably not!

The next scenario, however, is a different kettle of fish entirely. It was about 1 am on a Saturday morning in the West End, when this guy in his mid-thirties jumped in the back of the car, fuming after saying goodbye to his mate. "That's it, no more. I'm 'totalling' him. I'm deleting him from my contacts and blocking him from all my social media. He's history, enough's enough!" It transpired that once every few months for the past fifteen years, he and his best childhood friend would meet up after work for a night out in town. At the end of the night, they would always stop off at a chip shop, and every time, he would say to his mate, "What you having, Paul?"

"No, I'm all right, thanks, Chris."

"Go on, have something, it's on me."

"No, really, mate, I'm not hungry. You just sort yourself out, I'm fine."

And, regular as clockwork, as they were waiting for their respective cabs to arrive, Paul would get the smell and start dipping into his chip bag and say, "Break us half that saveloy off, would you, mate," and then complain that he hadn't put enough vinegar on it.

Now that, my friends, is rantworthy!

* Personally, whilst I consider myself to be a pretty laid-back, unruffled, live-and-let-live type of guy, as my family will tell you, there are a number of things in life that really get my goat:

1. WhatsApp groups. I have no objection at all to the principle of connecting up. In fact, I'm on a drivers' and old school friends' group myself. It's when somebody posts something and a short while after you hear your message alert. So, in my case, I may have a passenger on board, and for the rest of the journey I'm preoccupied wondering what the new message says. When I eventually drop the passenger off, I immediately pounce on my mobile and, with great expectation and excitement, open the app to find an emoji of a 'smiley face'! A little later, the process starts again. This time, it's a 'thumbs-up'! And so it continues!

2. Eamonn Holmes and Ruth Langsford. I like Eamonn. And I like Ruth. But I don't like Eamonn & Ruth!

3. Abba. I hate Abba. But I love Abba tribute bands!

4. Wind turbines. I hate those things with a passion. Not only are they monstrous blights on our landscape, but they make the surrounding area so windy. And I know it's them because the faster they go, the windier it gets!

5. My mate Steve. Steve is one of those guys that thinks he knows exactly what you're about to say and is forever finishing your sentence off for you. Invariably, however, he is way off beam, and I'm constantly having to say, "Yeah, but also..." which can be exhausting!

The little things that make life worth living!

Shortly after collecting a woman from the airport, she took a big yawn and sighed, "Aaah, that's better," as her ears popped and she could suddenly hear clearly again. This led on to a conversation about 'Aaah Moments' – the little occasions in life that we don't make a big song and dance about but just make us go "Aaah" when they happen. As a big chocolate lover, her favourite 'Aaah moment', she revealed, is when you thought you'd eaten your last chocolate button, and, then, to your delight, a little later on, you glance down to find one on the front of your jumper! Second that! (Although I do make a big song and dance about it when it happens to me.)

I then shared with her my favourite 'Aaah moment' – removing the family hair from the bath plughole! That exhilaration as you fill the bath up two to three inches and, for the first time in weeks, watch it flow freely away, especially that last bit when the whirlpool forms and you hear the gurgle as the final traces of water vanish out of sight. In your excitement, you call down to the family, "Helen, kids, quick, come up here a minute and watch this." They're not impressed! You're not discouraged! For the next ten minutes you remain in the bathroom, blissfully shallow-filling the bath and removing the plug, thinking to yourself, *Aaah, it doesn't get much better than this!*

I'm not a saddo, am I?

Competition on!

Every so often, I'll be chatting away with a passenger, one of us will say something, and before we know where we are, we have a little competition going on.

A couple that stick out in my mind are naming famous

siblings (the one I was particularly surprised about was Gary Oldman – Sirius Black in *Harry Potter* – and Big Mo off *EastEnders*) and naming singers with Andromeda voices. (We didn't get that far with this one, to be honest, and only managed to come up with Boy George, Alison Moyet, Neil Sedaka [borderline] and Barry Gibb [sometimes].)

To me, this sort of thing is just a bit of harmless fun that makes for a pleasant journey and is not about the winning, which is just as well, given the phenomenal knowledge some of my passengers possess. One guy got in with a dog breed I didn't quite recognise. He told me that it was a Saluki, a sighthound that hunts by sight rather than scent, the dog of choice for Middle Eastern royalty. A competition to name the most unusual dog breeds then ensued between us. As somewhat of a dog enthusiast myself, I was up for this one and hit him with the likes of the Norwegian Lundehund, the Sloughi and the tenacious little Cesky Terrier. But this guy was on a completely different plane and came back at me with names I'd never even heard of before, like the Golden Foot Locker Lab, the miniature M&S Spaniel, the Boots Black & Tan Basset Hound, the Soft-Coated Primark Terrier, and the shaggy-haired Newpoundland working dog. So superior was his canine knowledge that when I got home that evening and looked them up, even Google didn't have these most obscure of dog breeds listed!

My favourite competition, however, has to be the one with the bubbly, well-spoken, clearly highly educated young lady from the salubrious Dulwich Village in South East London on the way to a nightclub in the West End. So that she could get straight out at the other end where her friends were there waiting for her, she paid me upfront. As she was trying, unsuccessfully, to put her change into her new jeans, infuriated, she exclaimed, "Why do they insist on sewing up trouser pockets?"

I just casually responded, "I know, it shouldn't be allowed," to which she replied, "I like it. Let's see who can come up with the best everyday 'Shouldn't be Alloweds'. Five goes each."

"I'm game, competition on, you start."

Isobella – 1: *People whose top teeth magnify to a scary level through the glass when they are sinking a pint of beer.*

(Very prolific in the pubs around the Camden area, apparently.)

I can't say that this had particularly struck me before, but I kind of knew what she meant when she said it. Through no fault of their own, for some inexplicable reason, some poor people's gnashers just seem to amplify up to quite frightening levels, and, agreed, until such times as the breweries and beer glass manufacturers get their fingers out and start working together on a solution to this problem, regrettably, these people should be banned from all public drinking establishments with immediate effect!

So, a good one to kick things off.

Me – 1: *Yorkie Buttons.*

I wasn't quite sure if she would appreciate this one as the Yorkie bar is really marketed towards men and in particular lorry drivers. As it turned out, her father owned a haulage company, and in the early days when he was a lorry driver, she would often accompany him on long hauls during school holidays and they would both share a Yorkie bar. She agreed that the buttons just didn't quite hit the spot for a number of reasons, and apart from not really tasting the same, they were just that little bit too big to enjoy. She immediately came back with Caramac Buttons. Caramac is one of my favourite candy bars, and whilst she was absolutely right that the button version didn't quite cut it, this example was too similar to the Yorkie Buttons, so I couldn't allow it.

Isobella – 2: *People who use the abbreviation 24/7 and then explain it – "Everyone expects me to be at their beck and call 24/7, 24 hours a day, 7 days a week."*

I agreed with Isobella that it is patronising for these people to assume that you need '24/7' spelled out for you. However, because this phrase has been around for some time now, this rarely happens these days. So, unfortunately, for this reason, she lost a few marks on this one. Broadening this point out, though, what can be infuriating are those people that think they are impressing everyone with their cliché for all seasons. I recall in a previous employment, through factors beyond my control, once feeling almost at breaking point with my workload and being told by my boss to 'Work smarter, not harder!' Let me know when the kids have gone to bed, and I'll tell you my reply!

Me – 2: *People who continue with a sentence through a big yawn.*

If you haven't quite understood what the person has said, it can be awkward asking them to repeat it. If they think you might not have understood everything they have said, when actually you have, you have to listen through them telling you the same thing over again. Either way, irritating!

She gave a slight smile and nod of approval at that one.

Isobella – 3: *People who give their dogs human names like Martin and Claudia.*

I recall a few years back stopping for a chat in Sainsbury's with a new neighbour a few doors down. She immediately began telling me the problems she was having with her Donald sniffing the bum of the Great Dane at number 27.

It wasn't until about a minute or so into the story, when she told me that she had to take him down to the local vet that afternoon for his booster vaccinations, that I fell in, but no matter how much I try, I've never been able to look at her husband, Ronald, the same way since!

So, a superb example.

This girl's good!

Me – 3: *The gently spoken BBC newsreader with the soft, dulcet Welsh tones, Huw Edwards, whom the nation has taken to its heart. Except, that is, when he's covering a French item, and every time he comes to a French word, unashamedly launches into Maurice Chevalier.* You can just hear it now, can't you:

"Let's go live now to *Paris*, as the gorgeous, busty ex-glamour-model-cum-topless-base-jumper *Celeste de Bourguignon* jumps from the top of the *Eiffel Tower* and parachutes gracefully down across the *River Seine – ooh la la*, it's choppy up there today – and loops the *Arc de Triomphe* twice, before landing safely to massive cheers from the delighted crowds lining the *Avenue des Champs-Élysées. Magnifique!*"

Isobella, obviously experienced in these sorts of cerebral exchanges, complimented me on an excellent example, and I sensed she realised that she had a competition on her hands.

Isobella – 4: *People who use a food item and then put the container back with a miniscule amount of the contents remaining.*

The times I'm looking forward to starting the day off with my, now (thanks to Helen), new favourite breakfast – a delicious bowl of healthy cereal! I line the yoghurt, cinnamon, toasted almond flakes, berries and honey drizzle neatly up on the kitchen table and dice half a banana. Tum rumbling in eager anticipation, I turn the box up. Nothing happens. I steepen the angle. Still nothing. I give it a shake. Faint rattling can be heard. A thimble's worth of muesli plops out and into the bowl! I roar, "You've done it again with the cereal, guys. Not fair!" Deflated, I reach for the bread, eggs, bacon, sausages, tomatoes, mushrooms, hash browns, baked beans, black pudding and tomato ketchup!

This girl's very good!

Me – 4: *Wide-backed women of fifty plus with massive tattoos of butterflies spanning both shoulder blades.*

These are more prevalent than you may think, and can often be spotted hurriedly rushing through airport concourses. Isobella chuckled when I said this and confessed that her Granny Meg had had one such tattoo done two years ago to mark her seventieth birthday and, you guessed it, is an easyJet frequent flyer!

At this stage, we complimented each other on the very creative examples presented, and agreed that we were pretty much neck and neck. With one answer each left, I think she realised that she would need to pull something very special out of the hat to secure victory. And, she did exactly that!

Isobella – 5: *The 2016 remake of* Dad's Army.

Wow, she might have me here! *Dad's Army* is sacrosanct! However good the modern actors might be in their own right (and it had an excellent cast of Britain's finest), it's absolute suicide trying to go anywhere near recreating something as iconic as this. It just ain't happening, full stop! I was astonished that such a young lady appreciated this classic piece of television comedy history, but she told me that she loved the special times spent cuddling up with her dad on the settee early Saturday evenings watching the repeats, and the joy and laughter it had brought them both. Lovely story. I could tell by the wry smile on her face and the way her eyes lit up that Isobella sensed the sweet smell of victory in the air.

A few possibilities of things that had crossed my mind in the past came to me:

- When the ex-Man United defensive midfielder-cum-football-pundit Roy Keane commences each answer to a question with 'Listen', as if to say, *ignore everything else that has been said, the oracle is speaking.*
- Hotels that supply free shampoo but no conditioner. (Even a 2-in-1 would suffice for a few days till we get home!)
- The excitement you feel when a friend invites you round for dinner and you're really looking forward to spending some one-to-one time with them and just chilling together, only to walk in and find five or six other guests you don't know sitting round the dining table!
- Linked to the above, when the host asks, "Okay, so what are you guys having to drink – tea, coffee, something stronger?", the one that replies, "Oh, can I just have a cup of hot water, please?"
- People who have a good hard blow into their tissue on the train, and then examine the contents. (Stop it, I'm eating!)

Each of these ideas was excellent in its own right, but against the remake of *Dad's Army*, well, I wasn't even going to insult her. Reluctantly, I resigned myself to the inevitability of defeat and was about to throw in the towel and compliment a rather smug young lady on an excellent win when I had a massive stroke of luck. Her mobile rang and she began chatting away with a friend for the next few minutes. During this short recess, don't ask me how, but suddenly, from out of nowhere, a moment of sheer inspiration:

Me – 5: *Alexander Armstrong's Christmas Album.**

"You sneaky swine. Yes, that should so be illegal, a crime against the ears of humanity. I can't believe it, that's so unfair. You kept that one hidden away right to the last minute when I thought I had you. You mean buttmunch."

We both laughed and she gave me a lovely kiss on the cheek as she got out, which made my night!

> ***WARNING ALL INTERNET USERS***
> If you come across a link purporting to be Alexander Armstrong singing Christmas songs, do not click on it, repeat, <u>do not click on it</u> – It could be Alexander Armstrong singing Christmas songs.

Since my encounter with Isobella, I have come up with a whole list of other 'Shouldn't be Alloweds':

- Roast dinner on any other day but Sunday – Thank you, mums, we know you mean well, but it just doesn't taste the same!
- When you're out with a friend and they say hello to someone they recognise, and then, for the next half-hour or more, proceed to tell you everything they know about that person!
- People who refer to themselves in the abstract:

"You've got to be very careful the way you talk to someone like me, you never know how they'll react!"

- Big-time veteran stars (Sir Ian McKellen, Stephanie Beacham, Robert Vaughan, Honor Blackman, Les Dennis) that feel it is a badge of honour to appear in *Coronation Street* despite standing out like a sore thumb!

- Customer service representatives who don't quite understand the application of the NATO phonetic alphabet (alpha, beta, charlie, delta, echo, foxtrot, etc.). Rather than clarifying, "So, that's *t* for *tango*, *h* for *hotel*, *o* for *oscar*…", they just spurt out, "So, that's *tango, hotel, oscar, mike, alpha, sierra, bravo, uniform, charlie, kilo, lima, echo, yanky*," causing your brain to hurtle into a spin as it desperately attempts to translate the phonetic words back to their respective first letters, whilst simultaneously keeping track of their place in the object word, until, around the forth letter in, you've completely lost the plot and, weary and exhausted and not wishing to embarrass yourself, you utter, "Yes, that's right," and hope you haven't just signed your life away!

- People that don't smile at babies. (Charlotte gave me this one!)

- Women driving massive SUVs who barge everybody else out of the way. (Helen gave me this one!)

- Young married couples under the age of twenty-five who call each other 'luv'!

- ~~Chavs~~ Shoppers in supermarkets who, although some of them may well intend to pay, open and consume food items on their way round!

- People who like to tell you that their lucky number is thirteen!
- That friend or family member you dread telling when you've just bought something, because you know the first thing they're going to say is – "How much it cost ya?"
- Men who eat one Pringle at a time. Ladies, never trust a man who eats one Pringle at a time! When selecting a keeper, three Pringles is a healthy number, and, personally, I would say four to err on the safe side! Any more than four, however, and you've got a different set of problems on your hands!
- Women that have all their Christmas presents bought and wrapped up by mid-September! Gentlemen – big warning signs!
- People that hog the hand dryer in public toilets when there's a queue waiting to use it, and selfishly stand there until every last molecule of moisture has evaporated away!
- Posh, pompous toffs who wax lyrical about the gustatory wonders of rhubarb!
- Poor, hard done-by people of privilege, like the dear young woman on her way down to the family estate in Berkshire for the weekend, who opened up to me: "We might not have had much when I was growing up, but the one thing that Daddy absolutely made sure I didn't go without when I turned seventeen was my flying lessons"!
- People who jump in with the punchline when you're telling a joke. Every time I've deftly worked my group of friends up to the brink of raucous,

side-splitting laughter, and am preparing to bask in the warm glow of appreciation from a delighted audience, with precision timing, stealthily awaiting in the wings, like a tiger stalking its prey, hitherto silent and inconspicuous, my mate Steve looms poised to pounce in a fraction of a second before me to steal my glory!

- Feeling like a complete philistine when you tell someone that you really enjoyed the *Harry Potter* film the other night, to be met with – "Yes, the movies make a valiant attempt at transposing the broad concepts of the story onto the big screen, but fall woefully short of immersing the audience into the complex and, often, nuanced wizarding world that the author originally, and so wonderfully, envisioned through her books."

- Americans for using the unnecessarily embellished word '*burglarize*' instead of our perfectly adequate '*burgle*'.

- People who add an 's' to the word 'anyway'. "Well, anyways, as I was saying…"

As well as the 'Shouldn't be Alloweds', I also came up with a new category – 'We Need More Ofs', with the following example to kick things off:

More cooking programmes on Saturday morning TV!

Guys, we've all been here, haven't we?

You come home after a hard day's work and your lady is sitting in the lounge totally engrossed in one of those celebrity TV chef programmes. Nigella, Jamie, Heston, Hugh, the Hairy Bikers… are cooking up some exotic, mouth-watering dish. You say, "Aw, that looks delicious, hon. I'm famished."

Eyes glued to the screen, she offers up a cheek for a peck and says, "Hey, sweetie, there's a ready meal in the fridge for you. Just pop it in the microwave."

Chapter Eight

We're a Motley Bunch, Us Lot (cont'd)

Left of centre (cont'd)

You will recall from Chapter 4 that I struggled to get my head around what could possibly motivate a person to contact a radio station to request a dedication or mention for themselves. I just didn't get it!

Well, since then, I picked up a former DJ from one of the major Scottish music stations. Ross respectfully suggested that I reserve judgement as we never know an individual's personal circumstances. He recounted the phone-in one Christmas Day from a lovely elderly lady who told him that she was all alone and considered the listeners to be the only family she had! Ross felt both humbled and privileged to have been able to bring a little festive cheer to this dear lady on this very special day.

So, thanks to that chance encounter with Ross, I have

rethought my position on this issue and wish to apologise wholeheartedly for any offence that my earlier comments may have caused!

Although I may still not completely get it and, personally, won't be requesting a radio mention or dedication for myself anytime soon, for all the Stellas out there, unscramble this:

it for ! Go

Chapter Nine

Earth, Swallow Me Up!

With the number of passengers that I've carried over the years, you won't be surprised to hear that I have had the odd embarrassing moment or two in my time.

On one occasion, the guy sitting in the back seat, who hadn't said a word to this point, suddenly asked, "What did you think of the Arsenal, Tottenham game?"

Well, as it just so happened, I had watched the game with the boys at the weekend, and thinking how friendly it was of him to initiate a conversation with me, I answered, "Both sides were playing it a bit safe in the first half, I thought, but the second forty-five sprung to life when Pochettino brought on Dele Alli and Wenger brought on Lacazette."

He then said, "That penalty decision was a bit iffy, though."

I replied, "Yeah, a deliberate dive by Bellerin and it cost Tottenham a place in the Champions League. The ref should have been shot if you ask me. Back to the old goal-line technology debate."

Anyway, the conversation continued like this for a short while longer, until I happened to glance in the rear-view mirror to see the guy talking to his friend on his mobile. He was one of those people that, when making a call, just launch straight into the conversation without the conventional greeting – "Yo, Bro" or "'Hi, mate, it's Sam, how you doing?"

Get out of that without moving!

Then there was the fateful Halloween incident. All evening, my eyes had been affrighted by the spooky spectacle of groups of young vampires, werewolves, skeletons, witches, ghouls and the like parading the streets of London on their way to their parties. So, when a pretty young lady in an inflatable yellow pumpkin suit got in the back seat, it was quite refreshing and I complimented her on her original take on the theme. To cut a long story short, to my personal horror, she wasn't wearing an inflatable yellow pumpkin suit!

On another occasion, I really needed the loo. Of course, every single petrol station I went into either didn't have a toilet or it was out of order, and there wasn't a single pub or McDonald's in sight. I should have put myself on a break until I found one, because, to my dismay, I got a job down to take a lady home from Canary Wharf, Docklands, to St Albans in Hertfordshire, well over an hour away. Halfway along the road, I became really desperate, and the best I could do in the situation was to discreetly loosen my belt, unclip the trouser waist and lower the zip a couple of notches to relieve a little bit of pressure around the bladder area. The lady was really friendly and we chatted away about all sorts of things, which helped a little to take my mind off the discomfort. In connection with a current news story, she said that she couldn't believe the number of weirdos there were around these days. "Yeah, I know exactly what you mean," I said. "Sometimes, I think I'm the only normal person on this planet!"

When we arrived at her house, I thanked her for an enjoyable journey and wished her a lovely evening. By this time, I'd completely forgotten that she'd put some boxes in the boot and was just about to drive off when I saw the boot door lift up. I flew out of the car and rushed round to the back to help, only for my trousers to fall right down to my ankles straight before her eyes!

This next incident could have been very embarrassing indeed. Whilst spending a penny at a local hospital, after carrying out my ablutions, as I was heading out of the door, my eyes happened upon this notice on the wall, which I quickly scanned:

Are your tentacles clean? Wash with soap and water for at least 20 seconds.

Fortunately for me, just as I was about to head back over to the washbasin, a voice inside my head told me to read through the notice again a bit more slowly. Phew!

To ensure that my company projects a professional, quality image at all times, drivers are required to maintain the highest standards of presentation – suit and tie, freshly pressed white shirt and polished shoes, accompanied, of course, by exemplary levels of personal hygiene. By far the most embarrassing incident I can remember occurred whilst popping into my local hairdresser before a shift for my monthly trim-up. I'd been going to the same place regularly for years, so the hairdresser recognised me instantly and we began talking away like old friends:

Hairdresser: Hello, stranger, you haven't been in for a while. Hope we didn't cut one of your ears off last time.

Me: No, I've been working these ridiculous shifts lately and have had to go to that 'Cutsbar' place, you know, that all-night Turkish barber's by the station. They're not in your league, though.

Hairdresser: I can see that. I'll let you off this time, but don't make a habit of it.

Me: Promise.

Hairdresser: The usual?

Me: Yeah, that'll be great, thanks.

Snip snip. Snip snip.

Hairdresser: Do you still get down the Fatling?

Me: Yeah, I pop in from time to time for the odd pint.

Hairdresser: Did you know George and Lois are moving on at the end of the month?

Me: No, I didn't. Why's that then?

Hairdresser: They're going to manage a pub down in Dorset somewhere, to be nearer to their daughter and grandkids.

Me: Well, you can't blame them for that. Shame, though, it'll be sad to see them go.

Snip snip. Snip snip.

Hairdresser: That's true, they're a lovely couple. Anyway, the last time you were in, you were looking forward to your big day. How'd it go?

Big day? I've been married for nearly twenty-five years. Um, strange! Don't say anything, just get the conversation back on to small talk as quickly as you can!

Me: Ah, fantastic day. Everything went off perfect. Yeah, really lovely, thank you for asking. Looks like rain. What's the forecast for the weekend?

Snip snip. Snip snip.

Hairdresser: I think they said scattered showers on Saturday and mainly dry but overcast on Sunday. I bumped into Mel in the High Street just after the wedding and she was telling me that it was a big turnout.

Mel? Yeah, she's got me confused with somebody else. Easily done. I know that from personal experience!* Nothing to be gained by embarrassing her!

Me: Yeah, there must have been the best part of 350 guests all in, I'd say. What do you think of these climate change activists?

Snip snip. Snip snip.

Hairdresser: I'm sort of sympathetic to their cause, but I don't like the way they go about it. A good bath wouldn't go amiss with most of them either! Three hundred and fifty guests. Wow, I bet that took some organising.

I'm getting in deep here!

Me: Oh, I left all that to the other half. I did my bit and turned up on the day. Are you keeping up with all the Brexit shenanigans?

Snip snip. Snip snip.

Hairdresser: No, I let them sort all that out. There's nothing I can do about it, so no use worrying. Wise man! And it kicked off a bit with some of your relatives in the evening, Mel was saying?

Me: Just a couple of people who couldn't hold their drink, you know, the usual. Who've West Ham got this week?

Snip snip. Snip snip.

Hairdresser: I don't know, I don't follow football. Didn't spoil the occasion too much for the two of you, I hope?

Help!

Me: Things settled down after a while, but I could have done without it, know what I mean? Soon be Christmas!

Snip snip. Snip snip.

Hairdresser: Don't, I'm still paying off last Christmas! And you were going to Bali for your honeymoon, if I remember rightly.

Bali? I wish! We had a week in Lyme Regis in the pouring rain. You're beyond the point of no return now. She thinks she's doing a great job making you feel like a really important, valued customer, remembering everything you told her last time you were in. You're just going to have to brave it out and go for it. She's nearly done the top, so five minutes and you should be out of here and no one loses face.

Me: Yeah, we had fourteen nights out there.

Snip snip. Snip snip.

Hairdresser: I've always wanted to go there myself, but my Pete won't fly. What did you think of it?
Me: Unbelievable. Best place I've ever been. The scenery's breathtaking. Miles of golden sandy beaches. And the most beautiful turquoise sea you've ever seen. And the people are so welcoming and hospitable. Can't do enough for you.

Snip snip. Snip snip.

Hairdresser: Bet it was hot.

You're really up to your neck in it big time here. If you say anything now, she'll be absolutely mortified! Just the back and sides to go and a bit of lotion on top and you're gone. You can do this, son. Just hold it together for a few more minutes!

Me: Scorching, but not that humid heat we get over here. And there's a lovely sea breeze that keeps you nice and cool.

Buzzzzzz

Hairdresser: What about the food?

Oh no, she's scalping me!

Me: To die for, especially if you like seafood.

Buzzzzzz

Hairdresser: I love seafood.

What's Helen going to say when she sees me like this?

Me: All freshly caught daily. Every morning at sunrise you see the little fishing boats sailing off into the horizon, returning home at sunset with their bounty. Next minute, you know it's on your plate. Delicious.

Buzzzzzz

Help, I look like the last of the Mohicans!

Hairdresser: Oh shut up, Stu, you're making me really jealous now. And how is the new hubby?

Me: Lindy, can I just say, I think you've got me confused with somebody else!

---

* I know from personal experience how embarrassing it can be mistaking someone for somebody else. I once went up to a person outside the BBC that was the spitting image of Phil Mitchell off EastEnders (well, from the side view anyway) and told them that I was a big fan. Let's just say, she wasn't best pleased!

For most of us, finding ourselves in these sorts of embarrassing predicaments can be quite excruciating, to say the least! Not so for my friend Lul (Lawrence) from school, who was virtually impervious. Obviously, loving being the centre of attention helped, but, combined with his amazing comic prowess, he could turn the most socially awkward of situations around to his advantage.

On one occasion, when we were in the fourth year (today's Year 10), the Sociology teacher was walking round the class checking on how we were getting on with the exercise she'd set us, and Lul inadvertently called her 'Mum'. Instead of doing what any other normal, self-respecting teenager would do in these circumstances (crawl under the desk, pull their blazer over their head, stuff their fingers in their ears and holler at the top of their voice, "Noooooo"), Lul casually stood up and made his address. "Class, can I have your attention for a minute, please. A very embarrassing incident has just occurred, in which

I inadvertently called Miss Scharf Mum instead of Miss. Okay, yes, yes, I know, simmer down. As you will appreciate, this is extremely awkward for both parties. We would, therefore, both greatly appreciate it if you could respect our privacy and give us space at this very sensitive time, as we work to restore the teacher-pupil relationship. Thank you."

Lul also used this ability to incredible effect with the honeys. Now Lul would readily admit that, in the looks department, you'd probably pitch him somewhere around the average mark. This, however, did not prevent him from aiming high, like the time he went over to the 'pin-up' girl of the school in the playground and said, "Hiya. My mates just told me what you said about me, and I think you're really lovely too. And, yes, I would be honoured to take you to the pictures on Friday evening."

As you can imagine, her reaction was less than receptive – "I never said that. I've never even seen you before and I don't know your mates. So, no, thanks." Lul then turned to the lads and shouted over, "That's not funny, guys. You're supposed to be my friends. You've shown me up, that's one thing, but more than that, you've embarrassed this gorgeous young lady, and that's not fair. He then apologised to her for the awkward situation and walked away, face down, all 'embarrassed' and 'dejected'. But you know what, that Friday evening, bold as brass, Lul strolled into the cinema with that very same beauty on his arm. A lesson for us all there, guys!

Chapter Ten

Humour is a Funny Thing (or maybe not in my case!)

'Always laugh when you can. It is cheap medicine'.

Lord Byron's right, though, isn't he – we just feel better in ourselves and life is that much more manageable when we can see the funny side!

Don't encourage them!

Occasionally, people do things that we may find questionable, but however much we try, they just tickle our funny bones. This was the case with the two young builders I picked up from a construction site in Essex to take to a pub a few miles down the road. As we were driving along, we found ourselves behind a large van displaying one of those 'How's my driving?' signs on the back. 'Please ring 0800…'

One of the lads immediately took his mobile out and left the following message:

Hello, mate. Yeah, we've been driving behind you for the past five minutes along the Longbridge Road in Barking. You've kept within the 30mph speed limit for the whole time, so well done for that. You slowed down in ample time to allow a young mum with her buggy to cross safely at the zebra crossing. You then waited an extra few seconds as an old geezer with a walking stick approached the crossing, which we thought was a nice touch, although a bit annoying for us at the time as we're gasping for a pint after a hard day's graft building brick walls. Anyway, you indicated to alert drivers that you were going around a lorry that was double-parked and used the correct lane at the roundabout. All in all, we are pleased to say that we rate you as a safe and competent driver. Well done, mate. You're a credit to your company and an inspiration to other drivers on the road. Keep it up.

It's no laughing matter!

Every so often, someone will share something with you that is clearly a serious matter of concern to them, but from an outsider's perspective, has an element of irony or humour to it. You do your best to appear understanding, whilst desperately trying to hold your lips back from curling up at the ends.

I often used to drop home a young, flash-looking, wide boy-type fella from one of the large insurance companies in the city – good-looking, immaculately turned-out and all tanned up with plenty of gab. He would generally extend me the customary pleasantries when he got into the car, before spending the rest of the journey on his mobile to his mates recounting the colourful details of his previous night's conquest!*

The last time I picked him up, he looked sombre and dejected and told me that he'd just been fired from his job. "Oh no, mate, sorry to hear that. What happened?"

Well, a few weeks previous, the personnel director had called him into his office and said, "I assume you know why I've asked you to come in today."

He said, "Because Kelsey slapped me round the face the other day for looking down her blouse again?"

The shocked director said, "No, I am meeting with everybody individually to appraise them of their positions with regards to the company merger next month, but what you've just told me constitutes gross misconduct and I'm afraid I have no option but to suspend you with immediate effect pending a full investigation into the matter."

You can understand my conflict!

---

* This guy put me in mind of my mate Rick from school. Rick had the looks that turned the girls' heads – the chiselled features, the streaked blond hair with fringe that hung just slightly over one eye, the olive complexion and piercing blue eyes. He also had all the *ma chéries* and sweet talk, like "Baby, I love the way you're put together." (I can't really judge as my one and only chat-up line, 'What's a nice boy like me doing in a place like this', didn't really get me very far.) I don't know what astonished me more, his gall or the fact that it worked! You might imagine, with his striking looks

and magnetic charm with the ladies, that I'd be more than a tad jealous. Well, you'd be dead right! Anyway, I remember one Saturday afternoon, we'd just had a Wimpy and were bowling down East Ham High Street, when Rick said to me that he needed to pop into Woolworths for a 'bit of business'. He headed straight over to the toy department where he said to the pretty young sales assistant behind the counter that he would like to buy the big cuddly teddy bear on the middle shelf with the 'I Love You' heart around its neck for the most beautiful girl that he had ever seen. When his purchase was complete, he handed the bear back to the young lady and said to her, "This is for you." Before she had time to react, he winked, smiled at her, turned around and walked out of the store.

How did I feel at that particular moment? Okay, so, what you need to do is drink a pint of salt water straight down as fast as you can. Now, take the index and middle fingers of your dominant hand and ram them right down the back of your throat as far as they will go! Then, multiply the result of this action by a factor of ten, and you're beginning to get somewhere close to how I felt at that particular moment.

"I've had my eye on that little filly for weeks," he said. "The dust has been sprinkled. Now I just have to wait for the magic to take its effect!"

The following week, just before closing time, Rick had me hanging around with him a hundred yards or so across the road from the store. Then, at about 5.45 pm, right on cue, the pretty young assistant exited the store. Rick crossed the road and proceeded to nonchalantly make his way towards his next triumph, casually glancing in the shop windows and whistling as he went.

As he reached about twenty yards from her, I could see a beaming smile come over her face. *Oh no, he's gone and done it again. It makes you sick, the slimy dashington. It's not right and it's not fair!* Rick's chest puffed out and his step quickened. A moment or so later, however, a 6-foot-something, pumped-up-type dude embraced her and gave her a massive kiss on the lips, which she seemed delighted to receive, as Rick quickly darted for cover in Pollards budget clothing store! "Oh, Rick, sorry to see that! What a bummer! She seemed to really like you as well last week, and I thought you were in there for a minute. Oh, mate! Never mind, eh!" *Hee-hee-hee!*

In another amusing workplace scenario, a young guy in the office confided in my passenger that he thought one of the young ladies in HR was really nice. Doing the only thing he could in the circumstances, my passenger waited for his friend to go out for lunch, quickly hacked into his work Outlook account and sent the following email round to everybody in the section:

Hi Guys,

As you will all by now have detected, I have not been quite myself of late. This is because I have fallen deeply in love with Melanie from Personnel.

I have adored her from afar from the moment she joined the company six months ago, even though she, doubtless, is unaware that I even exist. She is the most wonderful, amazing creature I have ever laid my eyes upon. I dream of walking along the seashore hand in hand with her and snuggling into each other's arms as, together, we watch the sun say goodnight at the end of the day. I know I would be exceeding my station, but feel my heart will simply burst if she does not know of my affection for her and hope that one day those affections may be requited.

It is no secret that I haven't been anywhere near a woman for many a year now, so you will appreciate the anxiety I feel in making any kind of advance. I don't know how I would survive if my attempts were rebutted.

As you are my dearest friends, I would greatly value any wisdom that you may be able to impart in helping me capture the heart of this most special and beautiful lady.

Thank you so much. I wait in anticipation of your reply.

Rory x

You can imagine the horror on his face when, later that day, the following replies started landing in his inbox:

Faint hearts never won fair maidens
Find out what she likes
She can only say no
Believe in yourself, you're as good as anybody else, Babe x
Just say a group of us are going out for a drink after work if she'd like to tag along

You'll never forgive yourself if you don't try
Great rack on her as well, bruv
Women like a man with a hobby – bring some of your
*   Airfix models in to show her one lunchtime*
She'll eat you alive, mate. She needs a real man like me
For many women, looks are really not that important,
*   you know, Rory*
Get in there, my son
We can go on a double date with the other one in
*   there. I think she's called Aisha,*
*   Alisha, something like that*
Mike from warehouse has been sniffing around, so
*   you wanna be quick*
Just go for it, buddy

And do you know how the perpetrator of this prank got rumbled? He made one fundamental blunder – he was the only one in the section that he hadn't CCed into the email!

Fortunately, he told me, Management positively encouraged a culture of levity and practical joking to enhance morale and optimise productivity, and everybody saw the funny side. In fact, as embarrassing as this was at the time for Rory (himself a seasoned prankster), he and Melanie have now been dating for almost four months and are planning their first beach holiday together next May time!

This story had a happy ending, but in a different workplace environment, the outcome could have been very different!

So, if you're thinking of getting up to some high jinks at work, remember to plan meticulously – the devil is in the detail!

You do pick your moments, sweetie!

Used appropriately, humour can be a powerful and effective social tool. There have been a couple of occasions, however, generally when I've been under stress, that an unadvisable quip has blurted out and potentially inflamed an already tense situation.

One that stands out in my mind was the 5 pm pre-book of a businessman from Whittington Avenue, EC3. It was a tight one, but I should have just about made it, had it not been for the fact that I was busy singing along at the top of my voice to Randy Travis's *Forever and Ever, Amen* on country radio, and inadvertently overshot the turning. Because of major roadworks in the area, I wasn't able to do a U-turn and had to go right around the block, which ended up making me ten minutes late. When I finally arrived, the passenger was standing outside his building on the corner of Whittington Avenue, fuming and gesticulating like a madman – *his secretary had booked this job three days ago... a £50 million contract was at stake... his company would never use us again... he was going to get me fired and make sure I never worked in the City again.* He said that he had been tracking me on the app and had seen me pass the turning ten minutes ago. No use trying to argue, I'd been rumbled. I had no choice but to fess up and just hope he had a heart. I apologised profusely and told him how embarrassed I was, and that, when I realised I'd overshot Whittington, felt like such a 'Dick'.

Immediately it came out, I thought, *Oh, no, what have I said? He'll think I'm being flippant about it and that will infuriate him even more!*

About a minute of intense silence ensued as I resigned myself to being down the job centre first thing in the morning! Then, quite spontaneously, he roared into laughter. "Ha, ha, ha. Whittington, such a Dick. That's hilarious, the funniest thing I've heard since my ex-wife told me she was running off with her salsa teacher, Lionel. Such a Dick. Ha, ha, ha. Help, I'm gonna split my sides. Such a Dick. Ha, ha, ha."

His whole demeanour changed and he transformed into a really pleasant guy. Fortunately, I managed to weave through a few back doubles and we only ended up being a couple of minutes late in the end, which he was cool about. He even gave me a £5 tip for helping him get his life back into perspective.

Although this particular scenario had a positive outcome, it goes without saying that humour should always be carefully considered before employing!

At least I've got a sense of humour!

Although humour is a universal phenomenon, there are clear cultural differences on what elicits a chuckle. Us Brits, for example, love a bit of irony and sarcasm to help us through the day, but have you ever tried using these on the Yanks?

An American diplomat based in London told me that he and his family had recently returned from a trip to Sharm el Sheikh, Egypt, to celebrate his daughter's graduation with a First-Class Honours degree in Environmental Science from St Andrews University, Scotland. Whilst there, he had bought her a beautiful 'hand-printed' silk scarf for five Egyptian pounds from a market vendor. She instantly fell in love with it and thought it would make the perfect finishing touch for the charitable banquet at Lambeth Palace shortly upon their return to London. She was heartbroken, however, when, just as they were leaving for the ball, she excitedly placed the scarf around her neck, only for it to begin unravelling in her hands.

Trying to make light of the conversation, I said, "I wouldn't have that. If I were you, I would take the thing straight back and demand a full refund," to which he replied, "That would cost over $1,500 on flights alone. Plus transfers and accommodation. You could be looking at somewhere in the region of $2,500. Not to mention all the travel time, which, with my current work schedule, is out of the question. So, thank you, Sir, for your suggestion, but I don't think that is really a viable option."

"No, I suppose not if you put it that way!"

And then there was the uber-handsome (I'm talking Dr Hilary hurling his brand-new, super-duper, top-of-the-range, state-of-the-art, deluxe grooming kit out the window, here!) American motivational coach – perfectly aligned features, ultra-white smile, streaked, shaggy blond hair, tanned, buff body. He told me that he had scoured the West End for a pair of brown leather crocodile shoes for a convention he was facilitating the following evening at the Institute of Directors, Pall Mall. His problem was that he needed a particularly wide-fitting shoe, which most retailers couldn't accommodate off the peg.

I said to him, "Funny you should talk about foot size, because I recently had my feet measured for some new shoes, and you know how most people have one foot slightly larger than the other?"

"Yeah."

"Well, not me. The assistant said that I have one foot slightly *smaller* than the other."

He said, "Man, we are all unique. You need to know that there is not another single person in this whole wide world quite like you. You are an original. And you know, despite what the media and popular culture would have us believe, it's our imperfections that make us perfect. Isn't that awesome? It's when we come to that point of acceptance and can love ourselves for who we really are, warts and all, and not what society dictates we should be... that, my friend, is true contentment! I usually charge big bucks for advice like that, buddy, but I like ya!"

I thanked him for his inspiration and promised that I would make it my life's goal to reach that place!

My favourite comic American encounter, though, has to be the one with the big Nebraskan. As we drove, he told me that he was the president of Mann's Inc, a large US mining corporation, which had been founded by his late English grandfather some fifty or so years back, and that he was on a month's tour of the UK to connect with his English heritage and to see where it all began in Yorkshire. To cap his visit off, he was spending a few days in the capital before jetting back home. With tears in his eyes, he shared with me how, when his great-granddaddy had died in the Second World War, his grandfather, the oldest of eight children, was forced to leave school at the tender age of thirteen, in order to help supplement the family income. He began digging peat from the local moors which he sold door to door in the local villages as fuel. His grandfather's name was Peter Mann, and he soon became affectionately known within the surrounding regions as 'Pete Mann the Peat Man'. Within ten years, his hard graft and entrepreneurial spirit had paid off and he had created a very successful enterprise, employing in excess of thirty people. He knew, however, that the real opportunities lie in the USofA, and in 1961, moved his mother and siblings to Nebraska, where he purchased a coal mining plot, and the rest, as they say, is history!

The Nebraskan said to me, "Ya know, my friend, I've had the most amazing time exploring this wonderful, quaint little country over the past month, and absolutely love all those quirky British customs and traditions of yours. But ya know what, I still haven't had a spotted dick."

I said, "Well, if you do, I can recommend an excellent cream for that."

He replied, "That's very kind of you, Sir, but I'm a traditionalist at heart, so, for me, it's gonna have to be lashings of custard on my spotted dick!"

I wish I'd said that!

Of all the funny cab-related stories I have heard over the years, whilst on holiday with Helen in Budapest, Hungary* a few years back, this one, recounted by the sightseeing bus tour guide, has to be my favourite.

A local cab driver was ferrying an American woman around to see all the major sights of this stunning city. When they came to the Hungarian State Opera House, she asked, "How long did it take to build and how much did it cost?"

The driver replied, "It took five years to build and cost ten million *forints*."

The woman responded, "In my country, it would have been built in two and a half years and cost five million *forints*."

When they came to St Stephen's Basilica, she asked, "How long did it take to build and how much did it cost?"

The driver replied, "It took ten years to build and cost thirty million *forints*."

The woman responded, "In my country, it would have been built in five years and cost fifteen million *forints*."

When they came to the stunning Parliament Buildings, she asked, "How long did it take to build and how much did it cost?"

To this, the driver, by now more than a little irritated, replied, "Lady, I really have no idea, but it wasn't there this morning."

Inspired!

* As I'm sure you are probably aware, there are certain people who are sexually or romantically attracted to inanimate objects – a phenomenon known as 'objectophilia'. Well-known cases include

Edward Smith, who dates cars (over 1,000 to date apparently, so any young attractive cars out there, beware! This guy's nothing but a serial autoniser who will charm and woo you for his own personal gratification and then break your heart without batting an eyelid!), and the famous case of the American woman, Erika 'Aya' Eiffel (née Erika LaBrie), who 'married' the Eiffel Tower in 2007.

Well, I believe Helen may have got a touch of this with the Széchenyi Chain Bridge in Budapest. This is one of a number of bridges that span the River Danube between Buda and Pest, the western and eastern sides of the Hungarian capital. It was a decent-looking bridge, I suppose, if you're into that sort of thing (which I personally am not!). Let's just say that Helen became more than a little enamoured with this structure and would make any excuse to go on it and, considering she is ordinarily quite camera-shy, got me snapping her from every conceivable angle.

It was like, "Yeah, baby, you got it, baby." *Click, click, click.* "Now turn to the side and sweep those lovely golden locks back. That's beautiful, baby." Click, click, click. "Now pout those big, luscious red lips. That's hot, baby, real sexy." *Click, click, click.* "Now show us what your mamma gave you." *Click, click, click...*

We'd be at one end of the city, starving hungry, feet throbbing and fit to drop, and I'd suggest crossing over on a nearby bridge to find a nice little café to rejuvenate. She'd say, "No, sweetie, let's just walk up to 'Széchi' [right at the other end of the city]. The exercise will do us good."

As you might imagine, after three days of this, certain powerful emotions began stirring up within me. *How can I possibly compete with a suspension bridge?* I didn't say anything to Helen at all, but at 5 am, on the morning of our departure, whilst she was still deep in slumber, I quietly slipped out of the hotel room, headed down to the river, quickly checked nobody was around, and kicked that thing right in the stanchions!

Chapter Eleven

What's in a Name? (cont'd)

The more I think about it, the more vast and complex this whole subject of names becomes.

Have you noticed, for instance, that when you come across a name for the first time, you instantly begin to conjure up an image of that person in your mind? A case in point is the name *Marcus Gummings*. As I sat there waiting for him to arrive, a picture began to formulate of a dull, lacklustre accountant that works for a national charity – tall and lanky, with the sleeves of his off-the-peg work suit jacket a couple of inches too short for his gangly arms; wavy, slightly greasy and unkempt dark brown hair, with just the tiniest hint of thinning around the crown; top front teeth off-white and slightly tapering to one side; well-rehearsed, deep, honey-dipped, official, confident-sounding voice; referees Sunday league rugby and, work permitting, coaches on his ten-year-old daughter's football team. Well, no, the *Marcus Gummings* I picked up was a short, round, shaven-headed sound engineer at the Royal Opera House, Covent Garden, with a soft, slightly higher than average pitched voice, who preferred gaming to sport.

Another name was *Arabella Montrose-Blyth*. The first thing that popped into my head was a rather brusque, handsome-looking, aristocratic woman in her mid-seventies – attempts a demeanour of pleasantness to all but cannot disguise an overbearingly controlling nature that has developed over a lifetime of privilege, and disdain of the proletariat that exists solely to cater to her every whim; married to a prominent Tory MP that served in a ministerial capacity under the Margaret Thatcher administration but was forced from office over accusations of sexual impropriety with his eighteen-year-old aid, and now serves as a lord in the Upper House. Again, totally off beam. The *Arabella Montrose-Blyth* I had the pleasure of picking up was the sweetest, loveliest young Scots lass you could wish to meet, who was in her final year of a Humanities degree at Queen Mary University and had just secured a job with an organisation that works to improve opportunities for the most marginalised in a number of developing countries around the world.

So, as these examples make evident, our intuitions for predicting the characteristics of a person from their name are far from reliable. Here's one for you, see how you get on.

Colleen Mcloughlin.

Okay, so the person you are visualising is a tall, slim young Irish lady in her late twenties, with curly locks of auburn hair, ivory skin and eyes of emerald green; very attractive, stopping just short of stunning, perhaps because of a conspicuous mole or skin tag, or an ever-so-slightly prominent overlapping front tooth, features which, in a strange way, only serve to enhance her natural beauty; a reporter for a local rag, but recently completed her National Qualification in Journalism (NJQ) and is planning to move to America in the next year or so with the hope of working with one of the major news networks, preferably CNN (or One America News at a push), with the aim of becoming an anchor woman by the time she is thirty-five; been with her commodities-dealer boyfriend for coming up to six years but not sure of their long-term future together, as he's more of your staid, steady sort and does not want to live in the US, and also really needs to stand up more to his interfering mother.

Well, yes, as it just so happens, in this particular instance, you'd be absolutely right. This is the exact description of the *Colleen Mcloughlin* I picked up.

Okay, okay, yes, yes, well done, give yourselves a big clap! Beginner's luck!

Right then, clever dicks, try this one on for size.

Aramis Duvalay.

So, in your mind's eye, you will be seeing a handsome, olive-skinned Frenchman with a buff (but not overly) body, shoulder-length blacky-browny hair and a smile that no woman can resist; athletic and especially loves the more extreme sports like mountaineering, white water rafting and hang gliding, and is only ever completely at one with himself in the great outdoors; moved to England three years ago to pursue his acting career and has had a number of minor roles in some reasonably successful independent movies, but is down to the last two for quite a meaty role in an upcoming Marvel superhero movie which is due to commence shooting in early 2020 (at the time of writing), which, if he lands it, could transform his life and help him realise his dream of opening an outdoor pursuits centre in downtown Marseille where he grew up as a boy, to help equip the youngsters there with at least some of the skills, confidence and aspirations necessary for them to become successful, upstanding members of society.

You slimy wet wipes. That's exactly the *Aramis Duvalay* I picked up a few months back and took down to the Three Mills Studio in Stratford, East London for a screening.

I give up!

Right, Americans. There are some things that can only happen across the pond.

I picked up a young English lady that had married an American guy and was now living in Arkansas.* Her husband's brother, Todd, and sister-in-law, Mackenzie, had recently had their second child, a bonny baby boy, and both wanted to call him after Todd's late father, William, who had been such an inspiration but, sadly, had unexpectedly passed before he saw his new grandson. Todd wanted to call the baby William, but, as seems to be the trend these days, Mackenzie had her heart set on the diminutive version, Billy. Despite advice from close friends and family, and counselling from their pastor, Jimmy, neither was willing to give way and tensions in the household were rising. One evening around 9 pm, their seven-year-old daughter, Harper, walked into the lounge with her nightdress on, holding her teddy bear:

Harper: Why are you and Daddy arguing again, Mommy?

Mommy: Oh, honey, Mommy and Daddy aren't arguing. Right, Daddy?

Daddy: Yeah, that's right, princess.

Mommy: Come and sit on Mommy's lap.

Harper: Okay, Mommy.

Mommy: You see, angel, sometimes grown-ups get very excited when they're *discussing* things and shout at each other and use naughty words, and punch Daddy in the face, but that doesn't mean they're arguing.

Harper: What you discussing, Mommy?

Mommy: Well, we're trying to decide on a name for your beautiful little baby brother. Daddy wants to call him William and Mommy wants to call him Billy.

Harper: I know, Mommy, why don't you call him Billiam?

Todd and Mackenzie stared in total disbelief, as if to say, *Our daughter's a genius. It's perfect, why didn't we think of that?* And, thus, two weeks later, the bonny baby boy was christened 'Billiam Corey Jackson-Anderson'.

---

* Does anybody else find this irritating? – People that have been to the States for anything longer than a fortnight, who, when recounting their experience to you, pepper it with elements of the American lilt. The English lady above spoke with a lovely Home Counties accent, but when I asked her how she came to be living in America, she told me she had met her husband, Austin, in 2014 whilst on a six-month secondment with her company in 'New York Ciddy', accompanied, of course, by the obligatory upward inflection that elicits the nod from the listener of "Oh, yeah." I'm not being mean here, am I?

Conversely, have you noticed that when we visit the States, the minute we step off the plane, we begin to accentuate our 'Britishness', as if to say, *You may be the most powerful nation on earth, but you can't buy class!* During a pilgrimage to Memphis, Tennessee with the family a few years back, we pulled into a gas station to fill up. When the attendant heard me speak, she told me that she absolutely adored the English accent and implored me to speak some more. As a proud East End/Essex boy, I am ashamed to say that I spontaneously metamorphosed into Hugh Grant!

One of the standouts of that trip for me was discovering 'buffalo wings' – *delicious* doesn't even come close! I couldn't help feeling a tinge of sadness as I was tucking in, though, imagining that they'd probably plucked the wings off those poor little buffalos before they'd even had the chance to fly! That said, no taste buds should go through this life without indulging themselves in the succulent delights of a portion of buffalo wings. If you haven't had that pleasure as yet, you may be thinking that they're a tough meat, whereas, in actual fact, they have an almost, what I would describe as, 'chickeny' taste and texture about them.

Anyways, back to the topic at hand.

When it comes to name selection, I have concluded that, somehow, some people seem to lose all sense of rationality in the process, as seems to be the case of the rather refined young mum I picked up from Sloane Square with her young identical twin boys, Xavier-Louis-Pierre and Kevin! It was like, "Kevin, play nicely, it's your brother's birthday!"

And I think this applies equally to the names people give to their pets.* I recall the rather posh, pretentious, vintage actress-type woman with her Toy Poodle, *Audrey-Fiona*. We've already talked about people giving their dogs human names in Chapter 8 during my encounter with Isobella, but, if the double-barrelled name was not bad enough, this woman proceeded to conduct a proper full-on adult conversation with the dog throughout the journey – "Oh, look, Audrey-Fiona, at the incredible craftsmanship and detail on the roofline of that Edwardian building. It's such a shame that people miss so much of the amazing architecture in London because they so rarely look up." Listening to that for half an hour, by the time they both got out, I ended up just as irritated by the mutt as I was by its owner. (That's not fair, I take that back; they were both very lovely really!)

My favourite pet-name story, however, has to be the veteran rocker with his Boxer dog. This guy was a seventy-odd-year-old, mean-looking 'Hells Angel' type remnant from the '60s. He was virtually bald, with his one little bit of hair tied back into a ponytail, and half his face obscured by a massive horseshoe moustache. He was covered in faded tattoos (LOVE and HATE on his respective knuckles), wearing jeans, studded leather waistcoat and exposed steel toe cap boots, and sporting a lovely, shiny, silver knuckle duster on his right hand. As a rule, I don't generally allow dogs to sit on the car seats, but, for some reason, I was feeling quite benevolent on this occasion! As the dog lay sprawled out on the back seat with its head in the man's lap having its jowls rubbed, I could see by the undercarriage that it had just had a litter of pups, which was an ideal conversation opener. The man informed me that he was a breeder and enlightened me on the many characteristics of the Boxer (intelligent, high-energy, playful dogs that like to stay busy) and his very stringent vetting process for prospective purchasers!

When we arrived at his address in Stepney Green, East London, I told him that he had a lovely dog and wished him a great day. He replied, "Ta, geezer, be lucky," as he called his faithful companion out of the car, "Come on, *Butch*"!

---

* Just while we are on the subject of animals, I came home from work the other day to find the council putting up a sign on our communal green:

'Dogs, No Fouling'

I assume this refers to dogs pooping rather than going in for nasty tackles, as, I can honestly say, that in all the time we've lived here, I have never once seen any dogs playing football on the grass (just a few of the younger cats on their rollerblades, but that's about it, to be fair!). And, in any event, and not wishing to sound judgemental, most of the dogs around here can barely read anyway. (I blame the owners for not reading bedtime stories with them when they were puppies!) So, putting a sign up like this will just go completely over their heads and is yet another waste of our council tax money!

Warning: Taking a dog named 'Shark' to the beach is a very bad idea!

Before leaving the subject of names, you'll remember from Chapter 5 when talking about people with very similar names to those of famous people, I postulated that Sean Connelly may very well be unbeatable. Well, since then, I have chanced upon a passenger that may equal, or, dare I suggest, being slightly more contemporary, even surpass Sean Connelly!

And the name of this new person is:

Wait for it…

Patience…

It will be worth the wait, trust me…

David Peckham

Didn't I tell you it would be worth the wait?

Having wrestled with these two superb contenders over the past few weeks, to me, there's not a dog's breath between them. So, there's really only one way to resolve this:

THE GREAT BRITISH NEAR-NAME OFF

Who will be Crowned
Ultimate Champion?

Sean Connelly
VS
David Peckham

The Nation Decides!!!

Answers on a Postcard

Just one final observation on names. The origin of the suffix 'son' on a surname, as you may be aware, simply means 'son of'. So, sometime in the dim, distant past, Robertson meant son of Robert; Jameson, son of James; Johnson, son of John, and so on. Well, I recently picked up a guy called Mr Dobson, and the chilling thought crossed my mind – at some point, somewhere on this earth, there was once (and for all we know, may still be) a Dob roaming about!

Chapter Twelve

Clean Well to Eat Well

May I begin by apologising unreservedly for what is about to follow. Like most people, I find this subject matter quite repugnant, to the point, in fact, that I am fully prepared to campaign on the issue!

Because I spend the best part of sixty hours a week sitting in the car, and had drifted into the habit of binging on chocolate, biscuits and crisps throughout the day, Helen had become very concerned for my health, particularly the risk of developing diabetes and high cholesterol. She now sends me off each day with a lovely selection of tasty salads and delicious homemade soups, and has a range of healthier snack substitutes. I am now also exercising two to three times a week down my cabin, where I have a boxing bag, trampette and some free weights. I have to say that I am feeling a lot healthier and fitter than I did, and have lost a few pounds round the old tum area in the process. But, as we all know, keeping this up over the long term isn't easy, so Helen allows me a couple of treats a week just to help me through. Well, my guilty pleasure is the Burger King Flame-Grilled Whopper Sandwich (a ¼lb of savoury flame-grilled beef topped with juicy tomatoes, fresh cut lettuce, creamy mayonnaise, crunchy pickles, and sliced white onions on a soft sesame seed bun) – Food Heaven!

Right, so having just dropped a young Australian couple* off at Heathrow Airport, I was heading back down the M4 into central London, when I suddenly got caught short, so decided to make a quick pit stop at Heston Services. Immediately I entered the building, that irresistible, seductive Burger King aroma elated my nostrils, and I thought, *toilet then treat time*. Whilst standing at the urinal, out of the corner of my eye, I observed a guy exit one of the cubicles. He looked to be somewhere between the age of twenty-eight and thirty-five, tallish, overweight, greasy black shoulder-length hair, scruffy jeans, worn leather jacket and creased-up, stained Def Leppard tee-shirt. Pausing only for a quick glimpse of himself in the mirror, he hastened straight past the washbasin and out of the door. I won't tell you the names that came into my head at that point!

After carrying out my ablutions, I just about managed to reset my mind and, in eager anticipation, entered the eating hall, where, to my utter disgust, I was assaulted by the sight of the same guy seated at a table with a group of friends laughing and joking as, with both hands, he stuffed his Flame-Grilled Whopper Sandwich ravenously into his gob. Desperately fighting my automatic gag reflex, I rushed out of the building gasping for air, managed to stagger to my car, and sped home to bleach my eyes and scrub my entire body with a Brillo Pad!

Sadly, I know that such scenes are only too common and would have been witnessed by most people at some point during the course of their lives. I'm afraid to say that this behaviour is a massive blight on our society!

Clearly, for such people, who, for the sake of this discussion, we'll call 'Avoiders', it is to no avail erecting big signs saying:

'WASH YOUR HANDS'

For whatever reason, be it upbringing, education, pure laziness or something much more sinister, Avoiders simply refuse to comply with the basic protocols of toilet hygiene. And in so doing, by spreading their germs through everything they touch, they place the health of the rest of us at serious risk.

Armed guards on the exits may be a little excessive, but surely, in the 21st century, we can find a way of preventing Avoiders from leaving the toilet without first thoroughly washing their hands. Avoiders will no doubt argue that any such action is an infringement of their human rights, but this is one area in which our leaders will need to be absolutely resolute in the interests of the majority.

Has society let Avoiders down?

I don't know, but, because of the seriousness of this issue, I would strongly advocate for the provision of specialist therapeutic services in which skilled, empathetic practitioners can provide a safe, non-judgemental environment that allows Avoiders to open up and talk honestly about their aversion to soap and water. Only in this way can we start building the knowledge and tools we so desperately need in order to begin helping Avoiders to correct this ghastly behaviour and start to integrate as decent, respectable members of society. Yes, initially, this would require quite an extensive financial commitment from the government, but I genuinely believe that such an intervention would pay for itself several times over in no time at all, through the reduction in general population sickness alone. And that's not to mention the many consequential benefits of living in a happier, prouder society.

Scientific studies on the amount of 'toilet' residue present on the hands of people across the land show quite a wide variation, with levels especially high in certain areas. It is in no way my intention here to name and shame any particular part of the United Kingdom, as that, I believe, would be unfair and serve no purpose at all, and I most certainly would not wish to, in any way, spotlight the countrymen of my dear friends Wynn and Nerys Jenkins.

So, Avoiders, come over to the clean side. We'll be waiting there to welcome you with open (unsoiled) hands. And good luck!

On a personal note, as a result of the trauma experienced that fateful day at Heston Services, my GP immediately referred me for a course of therapy. I am currently eight weeks into a ten-week programme, and am very pleased to report that the severity and frequency of my nightmares is gradually beginning to reduce, down now to maybe one every three to four days. I must thank Helen at this point; she has been my rock throughout this whole sorrowful, depraved saga. I really don't know how I would have coped without her. For months, two or three times a night, she would be jolted from her slumber by my screams of "No, please, no, I'm too young to die. There's still so much I want to do in my life."

149

My heart pounding, gasping for breath and drenched in sweat, Helen calmly tethers me to her bosom (she knows when I'm faking it!), gently strokes my brow and softly whispers, "There, there, it's okay, baby. You've just had another one of those horrible dreams. That big, nasty Flame-Grilled Whopper Sandwich germ monster has gone now. Think nice happy thoughts and fall back to sleep, my darling. Everything's all right."

Although I am making excellent progress, due to the psychological severity of my ordeal, at this morning's session, my psychoanalyst, Dr Hassani, dropped a bombshell on me – I may never be able to face another Flame-Grilled Whopper Sandwich again for the rest of my life!

---

* There are certain experiences that happen to us every now and then in life that seem to defy coincidence. The young Australian couple that I dropped off at the airport told me that they were returning to their homeland after an amazing year backpacking around Europe. They recounted how, at the start of their adventure, as they were sitting in Melbourne Airport departure lounge, excitedly waiting for the flight to their first destination, Salzburg, Austria, with a couple of hours to kill, they decided to go for a Garfunkel's to set them up for the long journey ahead. When they returned an hour or so later, the departure lounge was pretty much standing room only. Fortunately, however, it wasn't long before a middle-aged couple vacated the exact same seats that they had been sitting in previously and they quickly made their way over to them. As the young man was about to sit down, he noticed the tip of something poking up between the two seats.

"Willow, look at this, darl, it's a passport."

"It must belong to the couple that just left. I'll wait here with the baggage. Quick, Hudson, you run after them."

Fortunately, the athletic Hudson managed to bound up to the unsuspecting couple just before they were about to disappear through their departure gate. *Pant, pant.* "Hey, guys, I think you might be needing this!" *Pant, pant.*

The man and woman pulled out their travel document wallets in which each of their respective passports was securely stowed. Perplexed, Hudson opened up the passport to reveal, to his utter astonishment, that it was, in fact, his own passport, which must have slipped out of his pocket earlier when he was first sitting in that seat! All that planning and excitement – it doesn't bear thinking about!

My own personal one-in-a-million encounter, or, should I say, encounters, happened a few years back. The occurrence of any single one of them in their own right, and I would have been dining out on it for years to come. The probability of all three taking place consecutively on the exact same day, however, I would suggest, is virtually incalculable.

The morning of Friday, 8th July 2017

It all started out like any other regular day. I got up at around 7.30 am as I usually do, had a shower, got myself ready for work and sat down for a bit of breakfast. At 9.15 am, I kissed Helen goodbye and headed into town to do a couple of bits and pieces before starting my shift, completely oblivious to the remarkable course of events that was about to unfold before me.

My first port of call was a 'fast repair' outlet for a quick tyre check. Following a thorough 'complementary' inspection of the whole vehicle by one of their 'highly trained' technicians, I was handed a report printout giving the car a clean bill of health! Astounded and delighted, with a smile on my face and a spring in my step, I then popped into my local pharmacy, where I witnessed, with my very own eyes, another person, apart from myself, actually paying for their prescription! And then, as I was walking back to the car park, staggered by the two preceding events, I was drawn by the sound of chirping emanating from an alleyway at the back of a row of shops, whereupon, after climbing onto a dumpster, there, in the eaves of the roof, I espied a nest of baby pigeons!

Over three years have now passed since those extraordinary couple of hours on that otherwise ordinary, pleasant, warm summer's morning, and I still wonder to myself – did it really happen or did I imagine it?

Listen to this next story, told to me by another of my amazing passengers.

About seven years ago, Lizzie, a twenty-eight-year-old criminal profiler for the Metropolitan Police, had just attended a two-day seminar in Peterborough on the latest developments in profiling software technology. Due to the seminar overrunning by half an hour, it was going to be tight for her to catch her 17.16 train back to King's Cross, and when the station guard blew his whistle, it looked like Lizzie, heavily laden down with the course pack, was narrowly going to miss it. Fortunately for her, however, a kind young man, around her age, saw her plight, sprinted down the platform and, much to the irritation of the guard, wedged himself between the train doors until an out-of-breath Lizzie arrived about ten seconds later. Lizzie thanked him profusely, before taking a seat, and the young man disappeared into another carriage.

After a minute or so to compose herself, she settled down and began reading through the course materials in preparation for a debriefing to her team the following morning. Try as she might, however, she couldn't get this young man, whom she had never seen before and would, in all likelihood, never see again, out of her mind. He had stirred up emotions in her that she couldn't quite put her finger on! Yes, he was kind-natured, a quality that Lizzie was always drawn to in a man. And, yes, he was very attractive, especially that lovely, warm smile; she wasn't going to deny that. But there was something more – a sense of deep 'connection'. She felt strangely comforted and protected by him! *The mind can be a funny thing*, she thought. *Oh well!*

Over the next few months, life continued as normal for Lizzie as she engrossed herself in her heavy caseload. From time to time, in her rare moments of quiet, her mind would reflect back to the kind stranger on the train, and she'd enjoy the feelings that accompanied it. So, you can imagine her reaction when, as she was walking along Embankment on a rainy evening, a sudden gust of wind blew her umbrella out of her hand. Just as it was about to fly into the Thames, a runner quickly caught it and, with that lovely warm smile, handed it back to her as he passed by. Lizzie's heart missed a beat when, to her astonishment and joy, she recognised him as the young man from the train, and those same feelings flooded back into her. *My hero.* Lizzie was a woman of science and fact, but the chances of this same stranger, with whom she felt such a profound bond, coming to her rescue, once in Peterborough and then again in a city the size of London, and over such a short space of time, well, that took some rationalising away! *I guess wild coincidences do happen*, she thought, but deep down, Lizzie couldn't help but feel (or hope) that their encounters were somehow 'destined' to be!

Another three months or so had gone by when, at the end of a particularly stressful week, as she was on her way home from work, Lizzie spontaneously decided to divert into the local Costa and treat herself to a much-deserved latte and nice slice of her favourite coffee and walnut cake. When she came to pay, however, to her embarrassment, she realised that she had left her purse in the office when the sandwich lady came round at lunchtime. As she was in the process of cancelling her order, a voice from behind her said to the assistant, "That's fine, go ahead. I've got it."

When she turned to thank her kind benefactor, she was shocked but, at the same time, not shocked, to see that same lovely, warm smile before her. *My knight in shining armour.*

"I think it's about time we were formally introduced, don't you?" the young man said. "I'm Phil."

"Hi, Phil, I'm Lizzie." Lizzie invited Phil to join her at a table, which he gladly accepted. The conversation felt easy and natural between the two of them, as if they'd known each other all their lives, and, before long, two and a half hours had whizzed by. She didn't say anything, but when Phil told her about a family holiday he had been on as a young boy at a caravan park in Kent called All Hallows, for reasons she couldn't identify at the time, a strange feeling swept over her.

As they were saying their farewells, Phil said that he would be having a Costa's about the same time on Wednesday if Lizzie happened to be passing by. Lizzie said that she may very well happen to be passing by!

Immediately Lizzie got home, she rang her mother.

"Hi, Mum."

"Hello, Elizabeth, darling. To what do I owe the honour?"

"Mum, do you remember when we went on holiday with Aunty Kathy and the family to that caravan park in Kent when I was a little girl?"

"How could I forget? It was the time when your father got the poison ivy and we had to rush him to A&E because his blisters started oozing puss everywhere, and that horrible site manager charged us a fortune for new bedding. A scoop of Daz on a hot wash and they'd have come up as good as new."

"Um, yeah. Do you happen to remember the name

155

of the place?"

"It was called All Hallows if I remember rightly, the same name as our local Catholic church."

This can't be. It really cannot be. Almost too afraid to ask the next question, she said, "And, Mum, do you remember I made friends with a young boy there?"

"Yes, I do. A lovely, gentle-natured lad, as I recall. He jumped in the pond to pull out your Cabbage Patch doll that you'd accidentally dropped in while you were watching Dad and Benjamin fishing for guppies. You were heartbroken for days when we had to leave. I think it was his lovely smile you fell in love with!"

Lizzie's jaw dropped.

"I know it's a long time ago, Mum, but do you happen to remember his name, by any chance?"

"Well, yes, I do as it happens."

Lizzie braced herself for the answer.

"His name was Philip. I remember your father remarking that you two, Elizabeth and Philip, would do a much better job than that other pair."

Lizzie felt a bolt shoot through her body!

"Why do you ask, darling?"

"No reason. Thanks, Mum. Bye."

Lizzie fell back on the settee in shock, her ears gushing, her mind in a spin. This was surreal! She felt as though she was living in one of those cheesy Hollywood chick flicks where, against all the odds, fate conspires to bring two lovers together.

She would have been about five back then, and her memory had faded over the past twenty-three or so years. She only had a dim image of the boy in her mind and struggled to picture exactly what he looked like.

About ten minutes went by and the telephone rang. "Elizabeth, darling, I've just had a thought. I think we may have a photo album of the holiday in the ottoman up in the loft. It's been a long time, but I vaguely recall seeing a picture of the two of you together in the playground. Unfortunately, your father and I are not able to climb up the ladder these days, as you well know."

"That's fantastic, Mum, thanks. I'll be round tomorrow evening after work. Bye."

Lizzie found it difficult to sleep that night, her mind racing ten to the dozen trying to process what was happening and what it all meant!

When Lizzie finally plucked up the courage to ascend that ladder into the dusty loft, the excitement was almost palpable. Would the contents of this box solve the mystery and provide the answer Lizzie so desperately needed?

After rummaging through old schoolbooks, tap dancing shoes, that silly red and white crepe paper Santa costume that Dad tried to convince her and Ben with when they were tots, she finally pulled out a red photo album. Would it contain a photo of the young boy, Philip, as Mum recalled? Would it finally reveal whether that young boy who had retrieved her doll for her some twenty-three years ago and the young stranger with whom she felt so deeply connected, and who had come to her rescue on three separate occasions of late, were, indeed, one and the same? Her heart pounded like a hammer, and she could barely catch her breath. *I can't do this. This is too big! I don't know what strange powers I might be engaging with here.*

Lizzie used all of her yoga skills to try and compose herself and still her racing mind. *Right, Lizzie, my girl, get a grip. Whatever all this may or may not mean, you need to know, once and for all, whether Philip is Phil, so come on, you can do this.* Lizzie counted to ten, took a deep breath and, with every bit of courage she could muster, began leafing through the album. And there, four pages in, without a care in the world, the two young lovelings, Elizabeth and Philip, sitting happily side by side on the swings. Even with the passage of time, Lizzie didn't need a second look. She knew instantly – *Nah, nothing like him!*

Chapter Thirteen

For a Job Well Done!

If a passenger is happy with the service they receive from a driver, they may wish to acknowledge their appreciation by way of a tip. Whilst this kind act is always warmly received, it is never something I either expect or take for granted. I completely understand that it is a matter of personal choice and that not everyone is in a financial position to make such a gesture.

From my own experience, I have found that it is your regular, down-to-earth working-class people, often on modest incomes, that take the greatest pleasure in treating you. I generalise, of course, but for certain groups of people, the very notion of handing over more than the contracted price is really quite objectionable! By this, I am referring principally to the uber-rich and QC magistrates!

Perhaps the worst of the non-tippers I have personally found, though, and this may surprise you, are the Yanks! The whole concept of tipping in America* is so deeply ingrained into that culture's psyche, that it is something that is done automatically and without question. For this reason, it is astonishing to me that this practice transfers so poorly across the pond. (Maybe it's because we don't chase them down the road with a meat cleaver over here if they don't!)

A couple of encounters stick out in my mind.

The first is the successful middle-aged investment banker I dropped off at his home in St George's Hill, Weybridge, Surrey (a 964-acre private estate, complete with tennis courts and golf courses – home of mega-wealthy entrepreneurs, Russian oligarchs and top celebrities, including Sir Cliff Richard and, if I'm not very much mistaken, former Hear'Say star, Myleene Klass). He told me that he has permanent residency in the UK but originally hailed from California.

When I excitedly told him that we were planning a Pacific Coast Highway trip the following year to celebrate our china wedding anniversary, he commended me on such an excellent choice of destination and said how even he, as a Californian, is still blown away by its awe-inspiring beauty.

He enthusiastically imparted some really useful information to help Helen and I plan our holiday of a lifetime. He advised, for example, that, as we aren't really great sun lovers, the best time for us to travel would be May with its spring temperatures, pleasant warm days and blue skies. The crowds of summer are yet to arrive and it can also be a more affordable time to travel (not to be sniffed at!). He also suggested that because some of the cliff roads are so windy and dangerous, it would probably be best to travel from south to north, so we'd not be driving cliff-side. When I told him that Napper Valley was one of the main places we were hoping to visit, he informed me of a much smaller, less touristy and less expensive wine-growing region (the name of which slips my mind for the moment) that was equally as beautiful. The saving on entry cost could go towards hiring a taxi driver for the afternoon so that we could partake of a little fruit of the vine.

One thing he insisted we try out there was a dish called *chicken mole* – chicken covered in chocolate sauce. The thought of chicken and chocolate in the same mouthful doesn't exactly sound inviting to me, and, as you can imagine, quite a conversation unfolded. I told him how Helen is always on at me for being so unadventurous with my food and missing out on so many culinary delights. "Trust me, buddy, you'll think you've died and gone to heaven!" Helen has also told me many times over the years that my general 'closed-mindedness' is also limiting my life's 'enrichment'.

Maybe this is why this guy's a high-flying global investment banker living the dream and I'm driving a minicab. Helen's right, I've become a creature of habit. I need to change my thinking and be more broad-minded and open to new experiences and start realising my full potential!

"Blow it, I'm definitely gonna order the chicken mole when we go! Don't knock it till you try it, right?"

"You won't regret it, buddy."

I felt strangely empowered!

I was extremely grateful for all this kind, charming American's time and willing help. After all, a man like this didn't have to do this for me, did he?

I generally don't expect to receive a tip from corporate account passengers as they are on work business. So, when we finally pulled up at his mansion (my house would have fitted into his garage with room for the car, a snooker table and some to spare), I was a little, but not completely, surprised when he asked me if I had change of a tenner – ten x £1 coins if possible. I felt somewhat awkward at this point accepting a tip, especially after spending such a pleasant hour with him. I began emptying my wallet of all its change and placing the coins onto the central armrest. As I put the last coin down, I was just about to say to him that a tip really wasn't necessary, but how grateful I was for all of his kind advice and couldn't wait to get home to tell Helen. At this point, he leant forward, scooped up all ten coins and said, "Thanks, buddy. That will help me out big time at the station ticket machine in the morning. Make sure you take that holiday, you hear. Drive safely now and have a good 'un."

"Definitely. And thanks for all the advice, really helpful."

Clunk.

Why, you tight-fisted dashington! I've been listening to you banging on for the past, seems like, ten hours, about how beautiful your dashington country is. Well, if it's so dashington beautiful, d off back there then! Oh, and whilst you're at it, you can stuff your chicken mole where it won't look out of place! Dashington!

The second American encounter, and this one tops them all for me, was the late-middle-aged, immaculately dressed guy with the slow southern drawl, that I took from his flat in Belgrave Square to the Ivy restaurant, Soho. The majority of the trip he spent in negotiations with an associate back in the States: "This is a $2.5 billion project, Chuck, with projected net annual returns of eighteen to twenty-two per cent over the next five years. If they're going to persist with all this 'nickel and diming', this is where I get off."

The fare came to £7.95, and the gentleman gave me £8, apologising that he didn't have the exact change. I looked in my wallet for a 5p, then in my back pocket, then in the glove compartment of the car where I sometimes keep a bit of shrapnel for such occasions, all to no avail. I apologised to the gentleman for the delay whilst I checked the compartments of my work bag in a last-ditch effort to find 5p. He was very understanding and said with a chuckle, "That's no problem at all. The ambassador will have to wait for me for a change. It will do him good." Finally, unable to find the 5p, I gave him a 10p instead. He thanked me kindly, told me to "Have a good 'un" and off he bounced, happy as Larry!

* I have experienced, first-hand, the power of the American tipping phenomenon at work. In 2002, a friend of mine, Dal, and I went on a sixteen-day East Coast trip to America. Immediately we landed on US soil, I could feel this overwhelming urge come over me to tip someone. Although I managed to control this impulse to some extent and just gave out a dollar here and a couple of dollars there, as appropriate, Dal, on the other hand, wasn't so lucky. After, I would say, about four to five hours into the holiday, he came down with quite a severe bout of tipaholia. When we would go into places like McDonald's and purchase a $2.99 meal deal, he would be handing over $10 tips.
The moment I realised that we had a real problem on our hands was at a toll on Interstate 95 on the way up from Washington DC to New York Ciddy, when

Dal was trying for over five minutes to persuade the operative in the booth to take a tip. The operative kept repeating, "Sorry, Sir, we are unable to accept gratuities," by which time a massive queue of angry, honking vehicles had amassed behind us, and we were threatened with security if we did not move on through immediately. At this point, I insisted on taking full control of the money. Dal, still in denial, remonstrated vociferously – "I can handle it" – but with our budget depleting at an alarming rate, finally, albeit reluctantly, he conceded.

Even after all these years in the job, the gall of some people never ceases to amaze me! There have been a tiny number of passengers that, with all impunity, actually want to make off you! With cash jobs, for example, if the journey price is, say, £17.40, passengers will often tell you to make the receipt out for £20. They will then give you a £20 note and say keep the change, and will claim the full amount on company expenses. There have been instances, however, when people have taken the inflated receipt and then only given me the journey amount! One guy had the nerve to get me to write out a receipt for £85 for a £48.50 job, and then gave me £48.50 (didn't even round it up to £50). In that particular instance, I told him that I needed to quickly do something on the receipt, and when he gave it back to me, I ripped it up, wrote him another one out for £48.50 and drove off!

Now outlawed, there is a psychological technique, previously used in advertising to manipulate consumer behaviour, known as 'subliminal messaging'. Essentially, this is an auditory or visual message transmitted very briefly, which is imperceptible to the conscious mind but can be perceived at the unconscious level.

Well, keep this to yourselves, but I am halfway through compiling an easy listening music CD with the sound of change jangling, notes rustling and the words 'big tip' spliced in at regular intervals throughout. I will then casually slip this on in the background when I am carrying the uber-rich and QC magistrates. When I have Americans in, I will play the version with the £20 notes rustling!

In discussing the topic of tipping, you will have noted that I have made every effort to avoid bringing the Scots* into the conversation. Unfortunately, however, for the sake of serious, rounded debate, I feel it is impossible to exclude them any further! So, in this respect, I recently purchased a CD of *Twenty Golden Bagpipe Greats*, featuring such gems as *Highland Laddie, Lament for Iain Findlater* and, of course, that timeless classic, and everybody's favourite, *Let's have a Ceilidh*! As powerful a behavioural influencer as subliminal messaging undoubtedly is, however, it is not a magic wand! So, when applied to the Scots, if I am going to have any measure of success at all, I know it is essential that I remain realistic. For this reason, I intend to intersperse the words *'20p tip'* throughout the album and just hope for the best!

Question: What sound could the jangling of keys being taken out of a pocket or bag as the car approaches its destination be easily mistaken for by the driver?

* The Scots are a very proud people, and rightly so, given their rich cultural heritage – the Loch Ness Monster, bagpipes, the kilt, tartan, the Glasgow kiss, shortbread and the Krankies. Their patriotism and sense of Scottish identity, as anybody that has ever met one will tell you, is almost palpable, and no more so than in the case of the elderly lady and her daughter that I picked up from a Fife brass band concert at the Royal Albert Hall. The mother had a wonderful broad Aberdeen accent that gave you a lovely great big cuddle, and the daughter had a thick Essex accent, peppered with the occasional Scottish inflection to remind you of her roots, like when she said, "I fink what arl do, Mum, is get up early in the mornin' and pop straight *doon* to Boots and get your E45 cream before that rash flares up again."

The daughter, in particular, guided me enthusiastically through her family history from the time of Bonnie Prince Charlie on her mother's side, and Robert the Bruce on her father's, right up to that fateful Hogmanay in 1984 when, in a drunken stupor, her Uncle Dougal had a serious mishap, recklessly tossing his caber, and had to have six weeks off work to convalesce! Throughout the conversation, she would intersperse statements like, "Your universities are some of the best in the world, that's true, but ours are free for our students, so they don't start their careers off in a massive pile of debt," and, "We have a zero-tolerance policy that has seen crime rates fall dramatically, but you're on the verge of anarchy down here."

I asked them how often they managed to get back home, to which the mother replied, "We haven't been back up to Scotland for forty-six years, since my daughter, Margo here, was six weeks old."!

Chapter Fourteen

Safety First!

In my line of work, first and foremost, above everything else, my primary consideration has to be safety! I am ever conscious that I have a potentially lethal weapon in my hands every time I sit behind the wheel of my car, and ensure that I drive sensibly and remain alert at all times.

If, for example, I feel my eyelids beginning to droop, I will immediately pull over and take a half-hour power nap to regenerate (which doesn't always go down that well with the passengers, it must be said – I can be a bit of a snorer!).

For many of London's road users, however, safety seems to be of very little concern. Throughout the day, I see drivers speeding, racing, undertaking and talking (even watching videos) on their mobiles, as well as cyclists jumping the lights and crossings, riding up on pavements and, alarmingly, the perilous new dare craze amongst young boys of wheelieing directly at oncoming vehicles and swerving off at the last minute! And that's not to mention the ever-increasing number of people riding personal powered transporters like Segways and electric scooters (also often whilst on their mobiles) that are currently illegal on UK roads and pavements. Add to the mix jaywalkers distracted by their devices, who just stroll straight out into the road without any consideration of their surroundings, and you've got a very dangerous blend of ingredients!

Warning Cyclists!

To all the ordinarily decent, placid, easy-going cyclists in London, who suddenly become completely self-righteous and aggressive towards motorists the second they get behind the handlebars: knock it off before you end up getting yourself a clump!

In light of the extremely challenging driving conditions in London, I would be the first person to support any measures to improve safety on our roads, that is, as long as they are proportionate. Some of the decisions that are made, to me, are absolutely dumbfounding, like the increasing number of London boroughs that have implemented a blanket '20 is Plenty' speed limit. I can just imagine the scenario. Hackney Council Highways Department calls a road safety committee meeting:

Chairman: Thank you, everyone, for coming today. You should have all had a chance to study the recent, independently commissioned Road Safety Report, and know that there has been a worrying escalation in incidents in the borough over the past year. This is obviously a matter of serious concern for the Executive, requiring effective, top-level management input, and that's why I've been brought in as lead. Due to its complexity, I'm afraid there's not going to be any quick fixes here, so I hope you've all brought your sleeping bags with you!

Ripples of obligated laughter from the members.

Chairman:	Right, okay, it's going to need some real blue-sky thinking here, so let's kick off!
Bright spark:	Could we not just simply implement a borough-wide 20mph speed limit?
Chairman:	All in favour raise your hands.

Chairman surveys the hands.

Chairman:	Motion carried. Lovely. Sorted. Right, Justin's going over to Prets. Anybody want anything?
Justin:	Am I?
Chairman:	Yes, you are, lad, and don't be cheeky or you can wave goodbye to this year's spinal point increment. Comprende?
Justin:	(*Reluctantly*) Comprende.
Chairman:	That's better. Now take the orders. Get on with it then.
Aiden:	Skinny latte and chocolate brownie bar. (*Whispering*) Hold in there, Just. He's retiring at the end of the year.

| Justin: | If I don't kill him before then, that is. |
| Aiden: | Get to the end of the queue, mate. |

It's probably the same mob that came up with the street names* on a new development I went to recently. I had to pick up from Duston Mews, off Duston Place, off Duston Road, off Duston Park Road!

> * Is it just me, but do you find yourself getting very possessive over the name of the street you live in? Say, for example, you live in Sandringham Avenue, and you're out somewhere and chance upon another street called Sandringham Avenue, do you think to yourself – *how dare you! What a lame, pathetic, good-for-nothing excuse of a Sandringham Avenue this is. The people who gave this awful road the name Sandringham Avenue should be obliterated from the face of the earth, along with that abomination of a street sign that is an offence to every poor victim that has the grave misfortune of clapping eyes on it.* And to any residents to happen by: "Oi, mush. Yeah, you! I live in the real Sandringham Avenue, not you, got it, pal? And if you want to make something of it, come on then, let's dance! No, I didn't think so! That's it, clear off! Oh, and by the way, tosh, you have my pity!"
> It's just me, isn't it?

One safety measure that I do have to give credit for, however, is the electronic speed signs* that display the 'happy'/'sad' face, depending upon speed limit compliance. Those things really work and their success lies in their simplicity! That warm glow of contentment that gently wafts over you as a 'model driver' when the 'happy' face flashes up, and the utter shame that suffuses every sinew in your body when you activate the 'sad' face! Genius!

* Helen generally only drives around locally, so I thought I'd best update her on the introduction of the – as it was then – new smart motorway technology and, in particular, the implications for speed limits. I explained how the speed limits displayed on the gantries over the motorways are set according to the road conditions at that particular time and are linked to the speed cameras attached to the gantries (although not every gantry has speed cameras), and the importance of still looking out for free-standing speed cameras, as you could easily get caught out if you just focus on the ones on the gantries. When I finished, she looked at me and said, "You love the word gantry, darling, don't you?"

Well, yes, I do. I actually really do love the word gantry. In fact, I would go as far as to say that, for me personally, of all the motoring-related words I know, there's none finer than *gantry*! Magnificent word! (Chevron comes a close second.)

Whilst we're on the subject of safety, this would be an ideal opportunity to pay tribute to our amazing emergency services.

I know I speak for us all when I say to our police force, our fire brigade, our ambulance service and, of course, our coastguards that we owe you all a massive debt of gratitude for the supreme work you do in protecting us and keeping us safe! For your dedication to duty, your bravery, your skill and your professionalism, we applaud you and thank you!

Occasionally, I have the very real privilege of picking up emergency services personnel, and am sometimes allowed a tiny glimpse into their worlds and the issues they encounter in the course of their duties. One young woman paramedic told me how, earlier that day, she had been on an air ambulance assignment to escort a young child from Edinburgh down to Great Ormond Street. The helicopter was scheduled to land in Regent's Park, where an ambulance was waiting to transfer the child the last few miles of the journey to the hospital. As the helicopter was commencing its descent, all but one man automatically dispersed to clear the way. He, however, was completely nonplussed by the situation around him and just carried on his leisurely stroll with his King Charles Spaniel, as if nothing was happening. The paramedic shouted down at him through her megaphone, "Sir, can you please clear the way. We have a sick child on board who requires emergency hospital treatment."

The man shouted back up at her, "Why should I? This is a public space and I'm entitled to be here."

She replied, "Because if you don't, in approximately five seconds, we are going to land this chopper right on top of your *dashington* bald head, so move out of the *dashington* way immediately, you *dashington* big sack of donkey dung!" He moved out of the way!

See, a soft word and a little gentle persuasion is often all it takes!

Talking with this woman, I perceived her to possess both incredible strength of character and real compassion for others. Knowing that her answer would be as honest as it was thoughtful, I took the opportunity to ask her a question that had been weighing on my mind for some time – Why is it that, be it a police vehicle, a fire engine or an ambulance, without fail, they always wait until they have pulled up right beside me before setting their sirens off full blast in my earholes? After a moment's pause and period of careful contemplation, she turned to me and said, "They probably don't like your face!"

Every one of our emergency services personnel is exemplary in their own right and deserving of our fullest respect, but I must confess that I do have a special empathy for our boys and girls in blue.

Recently, as I was sitting in a heavy rush-hour traffic jam, I was suddenly jolted by the sound of a siren blasting in my earholes and blue lights flashing. Panicked and flustered, we all started manoeuvring within what little space we had and just about managed to squeeze a parting for the police vehicle to pass through. A quarter of a mile or so down the road, I saw the policeman and policewoman exit their car and stroll into a Caffè Nero. I have absolutely no idea what was kicking off in there!

And I really don't know how our police manage to continually remain so kind and understanding with the public at large. I was particularly touched by one policeman as he pulled over a busty, young, blonde bombshell in her

Mazda MX-5 convertible and told her that she was going down a one-way street. You may reasonably have expected him to throw the book at the busty, young, blonde bombshell for driving without all due care and attention. Instead, however, with a warm smile and a little light-hearted banter to put the busty, young, blonde bombshell at her ease, he gently reassured the busty, young, blonde bombshell that she had absolutely nothing at all to worry about, as she explained to him, "But, Officer, I'm only going one way!" If my memory serves me right, I think he may even have given the busty, young, blonde bombshell his mobile number just in case he could be of any further assistance in the future. That, my friends, is going above and beyond the call of duty, and public service at its finest!

And, in the wake of all the relentless government cuts to our police services, the excellent work they continue to do is all the more admirable. Sadly, with fewer and fewer bobbies on the beat, I sense a real disconnect between the constabularies and the communities they are so committed to serving. I may be viewing things through rose-tinted glasses, but it just felt to me back in the '70s and '80s, growing up in the East End of London, that there was a much greater sense of solidarity between the two parties and a real feeling that, together, we can make our streets safer! I know times have changed, but even back then we were acutely aware of the resource limitations and pressure that our police were under. In fact, we had a slogan that soon became a mantra in our joint fight against crime:

'Help the police – beat yourself up'

Chapter Fifteen

Leading the Way!

To me, driving in London is akin to being put through the army's most gruelling assault course – surrounded by reckless road users on every side, roadworks as far as the eye can see, the invasion of the cycle paths, and vehicles proliferating at an exponential rate! I'm grateful at the end of each day just to get out the other side in one piece, albeit generally battered and bruised and a little worse for wear!

And, if you want to get anywhere fast in London, forget it! In fact, I once read that the average speed in this city is 7.6 miles per hour, slower than that of the age of the horse and cart. On top of that, if you're in an absolute real rush, two things are guaranteed:

Firstly, it will be bin day! And, of course, despite having plenty of room to pull in to allow vehicles to pass through, the dustbin lorry sits there between the cars parked on either side of the road until the very last bin bag has been despatched in the back, before moving up a further ten feet.

Upon reflection, in the cold light of day, I guess it wouldn't really be fair to ask those poor, big, strapping waste management and disposal technicians to carry all those heavy bin bags that extra ten feet just so that people (especially us personnel logistics facilitators) can go about their business without unnecessary delay!

Secondly, the two oncoming bus drivers will pull their cabs up alongside each other in the High Street for their obligatory *tête-à-tête*, thereby blocking the road in both directions for several minutes:

78 Driver: All right, Tony?

381 Driver: All right, Pete.

78 Driver: Did you get that memo from HR about the overtime ban coming in from 1st May?

381 Driver: Yeah, mate. I've been in touch with Garth, the union rep. He's livid.

78 Driver: I tell you, mate, that will cut our wages by at least a third. And that's just the thin end of the wedge with this lot, you mark my words.

381 Driver: You're right about that, mate. We need to stick together on this one. Solidarity and all that!

78 Driver: Garth said if they implement this ban, he's pulling us all out.

381 Driver: That's the only language these *dashingtons* understand, mate.

78 Driver: You better get that Corsica holiday in quick, Tone.

381 Driver: Yeah, we're going at the end of the month. Can't wait. I'm absolutely knackered with all this overtime I've been doing lately. I said to Kerry, "Better enjoy this one, babe. It might be Bognor Regis next year." What about you,

> Pete, you getting away?

78 Driver: Nah, not this year, mate. We're having the kitchen done, ain't we. We'll probably spend a week with Jill's mum and dad down in Rye, but I reckon that'll be it. I said to her, "We can still have some nice days out, though, darling." She loves all that medieval stuff, Henry VIII and that, so I said I'd take her to Hever Castle for the day in the summer, and have a nice pub lunch while we're out.

381 Driver: I went there with Kerry and the boys a couple of years back for a jousting tournament. Fantastic day out. You suddenly hear this fanfare and Henry VIII appears with his procession and pronounces the tournament open. We loved it.

I couldn't care less about your overtime, or your kitchen, or your holidays. (I might check out the jousting with Helen and the kids, though!) Just get those dashington buses out of my dashington way, now, you ignorant dashingtons!

As if the general road conditions in London are not straining enough at the best of times, add to this the selfish, aggressive boneheads* that deliberately go out of their way to be as antagonistic and hostile as they possibly can, and the driving experience can suddenly become very tense indeed. Drivers who, when you are about to pull out of a side turning into a main road as the traffic is slowing for the lights, get a thrill out of speeding up to block your access! Drivers who, when you are at an impasse in a narrow side turning, and you have made a big manoeuvre, backing up to let them pass through, make no acknowledgement of thanks

178

at all, but just drive straight past as if you weren't there. (Just to stress that, whilst courteous, the flashing of headlights or waving to say thank you is actually illegal, which means that these people are technically correct – how doubly annoying is that?) Drivers who, if you're not a quarter of a mile down the road a nanosecond after the lights have changed to green, fly off into a frenzied rage, gesticulating at you like a maniac who wants to cut your liver out! Sadly, such people are all too common on London's roads.

> * I am possibly being overly harsh to these anti-social road users, whose obnoxious behaviour may not be entirely their fault. It may just be their brain cell misfiring.

And to cap it off, as any minicab driver that has ever inadvertently parked a fraction of a millimetre over a taxi rank will tell you, we then have the wrath of the black cab drivers* to contend with.

To me, the taxi is one of our most valuable national treasures – an iconic, instantly recognisable global brand and essential part of the London experience. With their superior knowledge of the capital's streets, as far as I'm concerned, they have every right to walk tall with their shoulders back, chests out and heads aloft! So, why all the snarling and grumpy, hard-done-by faces already? To be fair, I guess in this ever-changing industry, they just feel threatened by any outside competition, and I get that. If we're honest, when push comes to shove, we can all become a bit territorial and protective of our own interests. For me personally, there have been a few times when passengers have made comments like, "The Uber app is so easy to use," or "I love Uber because you know exactly how far away your car is when you book," or "With ride-sharing, you can split the cost of an Uber journey," that I have found myself asking them to kindly tone the language down, as I don't appreciate four-letter words being used in my car!

---

* There's a couple of cab drivers down my street – an Italian guy, Jeffano, who I nod to when I see him, and my next-door neighbour. Whenever I see my next-door neighbour out washing down his cab, I'll say, "All right, Geoff, you can do mine next," which will always be met with a grunt. And if I ask him how business is going, it's 'dead'. The way I look at it, is that we're all different, so we've just got to take each other as we come, and try to rub along together the best we can. Generally, this works fine, but there is one really inconsiderate thing that Geoff does that I do find particularly hard to handle. Geoff generally gets home from his shift between around 2 and 3 am. Unlike most people, mindful of their neighbours pushing up the zeds at this time, Geoff slams the front door behind him and starts clanging pots and pans and setting off all sorts of kitchen appliances as he commences to rustle himself up a late-night banquet, all whilst singing (surprisingly well, it has to be said) along to one of his well-worn Bruce Springsteen albums. I tell you, sometimes the noise coming from that house, at that unearthly hour of the morning, is so deafening that I can barely even hear myself practising my trumpet!

Having experienced the relentless 'dog eat dog', 'me first', 'barge you out of the way' attitude of so many, for so long, sadly, I had come to develop a real disdain for all other road users. In fact, in my mind's eye, I had formulated an archetypal image of the *'other'* driver – 6'0", maybe 6'1", tall, thickset, cropped mousy hair, heavy eyebrow line, sloping face and slightly protruding jawbone. In addition, she has a completely expressionless face, with absolutely no emotion in her beady little eyes, except to display her anger at the slightest perceived highway infraction by any person that has the audacity to use the road at the same time as her.

Operating with feelings of such detestation towards those around you cannot be healthy. I recall one occasion when I was rushing to pick a passenger up for an urgent hospital appointment, and a man had the nerve to push the pelican crossing button to cross the road. I just sat there at the lights fuming, sneering at every step he took and thinking, *How dare you, you pathetic excuse for a human being. You slimy sewer rat. Slither back into the drains where you belong, you complete waste of space.* All I could think about was jumping out of the car, taking him down with a flying roundhouse kick and getting him into a Japanese stranglehold until he begged for forgiveness for pushing that infernal button!

Well, shortly after this, I was again rushing for a pickup just off the King's Road, Chelsea, and inadvertently overshot the junction by a foot or so, causing a young 'Sloane Ranger' woman in her new top-end Range Rover to slam the anchors on to narrowly avert a collision. I held my hand up to apologise, of course, fully expecting a barrage of, justifiable, abuse from the woman for my 'recklessness'.

Instead, however, she gave me a big beaming smile as if to say, *Don't worry, we all make mistakes, no one's hurt!*

The gracious reaction of that young woman with the big beaming smile that cold, rainy February evening put me to shame when I reflected on the outrage I'd felt towards the poor man for just wanting to cross the road whilst I happened to be passing through! She would, doubtless, have long forgotten this incident, and will never know the profound impact it had on me. Things just suddenly clicked into perspective. I may not be able to change the road conditions or other people, but I can certainly change my own attitudes and behaviour! There and then, I decided to make a stand and try my very best to be a positive influence on the roads of London – '*Be the Difference*'! Although I won't deny the odd lapse from time to time, my primary motivation at the start of each working day is now to be as courteous and accommodating as I possibly can to those I will be sharing the road with, regardless of their conduct towards me, accompanied, of course, by a big beaming smile! And, I am proud to say, this applies equally to the black cabbies. In fact, I would say that I often afford them an even greater level of politeness and respect. In so doing, I must confess, I can often feel quite sorry for them! The expression of sheer agony on their faces when, as if fighting through thick treacle, their arm raises arduously up through the excruciating pain barrier to offer a slight wave of appreciation for a friendly gesture from the 'enemy' with the big beaming smile – that isn't easy to watch! I've had people in the past suggest to me that I do this deliberately just to watch them squirm. To such people, I simply say this: "Who? Me? Never!"

And, do you know the most wonderful thing that I've found? – Kindness is infectious! When people are shown an act of kindness, oftentimes, they will pass on a kindness to another in turn, sometimes setting off a chain reaction. This is a wonderful phenomenon to behold but can backfire on you. For instance, when in a queue of traffic on a main road, I will generally ease up to let a car out of a side turning. That driver, appreciating the thought, will often then allow another car out at the next turning, and so the process continues, until, before I know where I am, I'm fifteen minutes late for my pick-up, totally stressed out and vowing never ever to let another person out of a side turning again for as long as I live!

In the grander scheme of things, though, with its amazing cumulative effect, can you imagine the difference if even a small number of people decided to give it a go and put other road users first? The amount of road rage incidents would plummet; everyone would still get to where they're going just as quick, if not quicker; the general driving experience would be that much calmer and more pleasant; and we'd all have big beaming smiles on our faces! Sounds utopian, but it's not impossible! We do need to be mindful, however, of one potential risk, were the 'cordial' balance to tip too far the other way. This was drawn to my attention by a passenger up from a small town in Wiltshire, who cited the example of two retired middle-class, male, otherwise model drivers, at a standoff, trying to pass each other from opposite directions in the High Street:

Driver 1 flashes to allow Driver 2 to go through first.
Driver 2 flashes to allow Driver 1 to go through first.
Driver 1 flashes again to allow Driver 2 through first.
Driver 2 in turn flashes to allow Driver 1 through first.

A period of twenty to thirty seconds ensues in which both drivers sit, stiff-armed, clasping their steering wheels, doggedly staring each other out, both resolute not to be the first through.

Driver 1 finally breaks the deadlock by motioning with his hands for Driver 2 to go through first. Driver 2 motions back for Driver 1 to go through first.

Fuming, Driver 1 gets out of his car and storms up to Driver 2.

Driver 1: Are you gonna go through first, or what?

Driver 2, equally fuming, gets out of his car and rears up at Driver 1.

Driver 2: No, you go first.

Battle then commences as both men wrestle each other to the ground.

Driver 1 has Driver 2 in a half-nelson.

Driver 1: Now are you gonna go first?

Driver 2: Hell will freeze over before I go first.

Driver 2 manages to swivel round just enough to poke Driver 1 in the left eye with his index finger.

Driver 1: Ow, my retina, I have blurred vision.

Driver 2 struggles to his feet, clambers over to his car and shouts out of the window.

Driver 2: Perhaps you'll learn to go first next time.
Driver 1: You've not heard the last of this. I'll have you, I
         will, if it's the last thing I do, you miscreant.
Driver 2: In your dreams, sucker!

Driver 2 then reverses and detours all around the back streets to ensure that he doesn't have to pass Driver 1.

Overall, from my own personal experience, I genuinely do believe that a little civility on the road can go a long way to improving the driving experience of everyone. Don't get me wrong; I still have days when all my buttons have been well and truly pushed and I can feel myself on the brink of a mighty eruption. Fortunately, over the years, I have developed an effective coping mechanism for such times, in which my mind drifts off into that perfect world of garrotting the driver in front, cute little puppy dogs and free cake!

All this said, I think we must also face the fact that there will always be the small few for whom the considerate, amiable approach will, sadly, be to no avail!

Whilst waiting at the traffic lights, I observed a Ford Focus that had inadvertently gotten into the left filter lane and was indicating to move across into the right-hand lane. When the lights changed, the driver of a flash Merc in the right lane (a big, thickset, shaven-headed, tattooed man) was busy texting on his mobile, so, after a moment or two, the Ford Focus driver just pulled across and in front of him. When the flash Merc driver looked up and saw this, he flew into a fit of rage and, for the following half a mile or so until we stopped at the next set of lights, glued his hand on the beeper and flashed the Ford Focus driver repeatedly. The Ford Focus driver held his hand up and put his hazards on to acknowledge and thank the flash Merc driver, but this was never going to allay the flash Merc driver's anger. Thuggery at its ugliest!

At the junction, the Ford Focus driver (a regular-looking fella of average height and build) got out, calmly walked back to the frenzied flash Merc driver waving his fists and snarling at him like a crazed animal. As the flash Merc driver wound down his window and proceeded to unleash a tirade of vile expletives and threats at the Ford Focus driver, the Ford Focus driver coolly reached into the car, somewhere around the flash Merc driver's neck area, whereupon the flash Merc driver's head instantly dropped and he was out like a light! The Ford Focus driver then turned, walked casually back to his car, at no point responding to the excited clapping and cheering from me and the other astonished onlookers, and simply continued on his way.

This guy obviously knew what he was doing. In fact, as he drove off, I noticed an oriental sticker in his back window, so I assume he was some kind of martial arts expert and had got the flash Merc driver in a pressure hold which made him pass out temporarily.

A lesson here for all the bullies out there – You never know who you are picking on!*

* The following incident should serve as an additional warning to bullies – you never know who's around! I was on the last train home on the Central Line one Saturday evening, when two young guys

standing by the doors started being quite insulting and offensive to another young guy. From first impressions, it seemed like the three of them were mates having the sort of banter you might expect after a night out drinking. After a couple of stops, however, it became quite apparent that they weren't all together, and that the two guys were deliberately intimidating and trying to provoke the other guy, creating a very uncomfortable situation for him and the rest of the carriage. As this was all going on, a Scottish fella in his tartan cap and scarf, about 5' 5" tall and wide, sat quietly with his head buried in the *Metro*. Well, as the doors opened at Stepney Green, showing no emotion or intent whatsoever, he carefully placed his paper down, got up, walked over to the two bullyboys, grabbed them simultaneously by the scruffs of their necks, lobbed them both off the train, guarded the doors until they shut, returned to his seat and continued reading his paper! Whoop, whoop, you da man!

As impressive as both of these scenarios are, I am in no way condoning any form of physical altercation as a means of resolving difficult situations – 'anger begets anger'! That said, in my mind's eye, I have designed a fully loaded 'Bond-style' car* to be deployed in certain particularly extreme cases. So, for:

    a.   the businessman in the dapper suit, chewing away and rather loudly giving it all the high finance on his mobile to Hong Kong, then deliberately sticking his gum to the back of my seat – a high-impact, spring-loaded boot to the backside upon egress from the car!

b.   the young woman hustler who saw the nameboard in the car window and pretended to be my passenger to get a free ride, after telling me her destination had changed, and then proceeded to casually chat away with her friend on the phone about meeting up in Milan for a few days – an ear-piercing sonic beam targeted at her head at periodic times during the day whenever the fancy grabs me.

c.   the lazy, sullen-looking guy with his baseball cap round the wrong way, trying to look hard in front of his girlfriend, who couldn't be bothered to take his supermarket trolley back to the trolley dock, making me have to get out and do it before I could pull into the space – a mind manipulator that causes him to be overly helpful by taking all the trolleys back, picking up litter in the car park and helping people to load their shopping into their cars.

d.   the pedestrian on his mobile phone whom I gently tooted as he stepped out into the road to alert him that I was behind him in a silent hybrid car, who proceeded to call me all the *dashingtons* under the sun – an extendable electronic arm equipped with a big bar of soap and scrubbing brush to wash his mouth out!

e.   the thickset tattooed truck driver who screamed at me until he was blood-shot red in the face, because I was attempting to change lanes on a roundabout – the launch of a tickling stick drone:

Truck driver:	Ooh, ooh, ooh, ah, ah, ah… get off me.
Me:	Are you going to be nice?
Truck driver:	No, get off me, you *dashington dashington*. Ooh, ah, hee-hee.
Me:	Then more tickles for you.
Truck driver:	Ooh, hee, all right, all right.
Me:	No more Mr Angry?
Truck driver:	Ooh, ah, okay.

Tickling stops.

Truck driver:	You *dashington dashington*. I'll *dashington* smash you to bits.

Tickling resumes.

Truck driver:	Ooh, ah, okay, okay, you win. No more Mr Angry.
Me:	Promise?
Truck driver:	Yes, promise.
Me:	Now doesn't that feel better?

There are several specific categories for whom the 'wet, floppy fish' implement would be used for slapping people around the chops. The exact number of times and ferocity of the slaps would be calculated on an individual basis by a sophisticated onboard computer algorithm that would factor in variables such as intention, severity, contrition and pimples.

These include:

- people who congregate around zebra crossings with no intention of crossing over, but, who, in so doing, cause me to have to stop and look like a complete twerp.

- business executives who derive a sense of power from keeping cabs waiting for as long as they possibly can, and do not have the courtesy to apologise when they finally do get in.
- traffic wardens who lie in wait during the school run, eager to pounce on parents who are unable to park anywhere else for that ten-minute period.
- Millwall supporters.

I also have the blueprints in my head for a number of more 'gruesome' gadgets. These are largely modern-day revamps of tried and tested medieval techniques, designed with three specific-use cases in mind:

1. our local milkman who pulls his float up along the street at 3 am every weekday morning with his radio blaring out Capital Xtra hip hop songs.
2. the woman with the big 4X4 in the busy petrol station at rush hour who decided to leave her car at the pump after filling up whilst she went into the store to pay, and do her weekly grocery shop whilst she was about it.
3. my mate Steve.

To complete my Bond-style car, I would incorporate one further feature – a volume regulator that would automatically drop the sound level of our friends from across the pond speaking on their cells, by just a notch or ten!

* Like most teenage boys, my school friends and I dreamt of one day driving an Aston Martin, a Lotus, a Ferrari, a Lamborghini or Bugatti. From the age of around fourteen, however, Des (in all other ways the coolest guy in the year, without question) became obsessed with Vauxhalls. When we were about nineteen, Des went into hibernation for the best part of three months over the spring, whilst he and his dad spent every spare minute they had building a beach buggy in their backyard. You can imagine our excitement the day we received the call from Des to say that the 'Desonator' was complete and he'd be picking the lads up Friday evening for a cruise along Southend Seafront, and our reaction when he rocks up in a Vauxhall Nova with the roof lopped off, extra wide alloy wheels, bucket seats and small leather steering wheel, and having to discreetly duck down every time he sounded off the air horns when we passed a group of girls! Give Des his due, though, he is now International Sales Director for Vauxhall Motors, and lives in an amazing place in Loughton, Essex, not too far from Rod Stewart and Penny Lancaster, who have been known to pop round on occasion!

Finally, before leaving the subject of London driving, I think it is important to point out that, in a city as diverse as this, there can often be cultural confusions, as different countries may have very different driving conventions and protocols to those of the UK. For example, it is standard practice in some countries to toot to alert other drivers of potential danger, which here would generally be interpreted as an act of hostility and could, unintentionally, precipitate an aggressive reaction. One of my passengers came up with a simple but ingenious solution to this particular problem that vehicle manufacturers may do well to consider – a 'nice' (yoo hoo, I'm coming through hoo) horn and a 'nasty' (get out of my *dashington* way, you *dashington dashington*, before I rip your *dashington* head off) horn. At least that way, there wouldn't be any misunderstandings!

Chapter Sixteen

The Road Ahead!

Well, it's coming up to fifteen years now since I nervously picked up my very first passenger – a real baptism of fire, that was! He was one of your privileged, entitled, air-of-authority Mr Nasty types, looking for any excuse to put me in my place in no uncertain terms. Unfortunately, the satnav I was using at the time didn't make the best route choice to Heathrow Airport, which meant that we arrived ten minutes or so later than we should have, resulting in a slight chance that he might not have sufficient time, after his restaurant meal, to do all of his duty-free shopping before departure. I apologised profusely, of course, but he wasn't going to give me an inch and, after a volley of insults, threatened to make a complaint to my company for all the inconvenience I had caused him. Not exactly what you need on your first day! In fact, even after all these years, my stomach still churns every time I pass by his street in Finsbury Park, North London. My enduring mental image of this man is that he looked like a thumb!

A lot of water has passed under the bridge since then, with all its ebbs and flows! Overall, however, I must say that minicabbing has served me pretty well. I may still be a way off from making my first million, but it has enabled me to balance my work and home life, meet many wonderful people and have a lot of laughs along the way. And who can ask for more than that in a job?

As much as I enjoy what I do, do I really want to see out my working days despatching people around London? – Probably not! In fact, I've recently been toying with the idea of making a fortune as a 'social influencer', sharing my amazing range of all-age, fun-packed, creative, eco-friendly bath plughole-unblocking hacks! But until such times as I go viral as an internet sensation, London will just have to continue to put up with me!

With all the exponential technological advancements that we're seeing in the automotive industry, however, the future shape of the people-carrying sector is far from clear. My company, for example, is planning to introduce a small fleet of automated minicabs onto London's roads within the next couple of years. To our relief, the company has stressed that the drivers 'are the backbone of the business' and that there will 'always be a place' for us. This is very reassuring to hear, but if the programme of driverless cars proves successful and continues to be rolled out, I imagine that our role will gradually change from that of driver to one of 'steward', with an emphasis on standout service delivery, in which passengers are treated to the most amazing, exemplary journey experience ever! I'm speculating that we will be provided with home teeth-whitening kits and, where necessary, clip-on dental veneers, in order to generate that extra radiant greeting smile for a guilt-edged first impression!

In addition to a comprehensive en route tour guide service – "We will soon be approaching the prestigious *Green Flag*-awarded Hackney Downs, opened as a public park in the heart of the borough in 1884 and boasting a range of newly refurbished facilities, including a pavilion containing two team changing rooms and a community room, which is available for hire at amazing rates through our exclusive London Borough of Hackney partnership scheme. Please contact our friendly, experienced Customer Services team for further details, and they'll be very happy to assist you with all your forthcoming event needs" – I also anticipate an expectation upon stewards to be well versed in classic literature (*Pride and Prejudice* by Jane Austen, *To Kill a Mockingbird* by Harper Lee, *The Great Gatsby* by Scott Fitzgerald, *Brave New World* by Aldous Huxley, *Harry Potter and the Philosopher's Stone* by JK Rowling, and so on) for the ultimate in scintillating conversation for the more culturally discerning passenger palate!

In order to secure a competitive edge in this extremely cut-throat business, my company will also, no doubt, consider offering a range of optional, bespoke in-car services. I can foresee myself, for example, serving up a selection of light snacks accompanied by a beverage of choice, filling the air with the sweet aroma of beautifully scented essential oils, neatening the passengers up with a quick trim, pampering them with a nice manicure/ pedicure, and finishing them off with a lovely, relaxing Indian head massage and shoulder rub to gently ease away all those nasty stresses of the day!

Who knows?

Chapter Seventeen

Arrived at Drop-Off

Well, guys, we'll shortly be arriving at our destination, and I hope that you have all had a pleasant trip!

So, now, next time you're in London and you see a stressed-out minicab driver frantically wrestling to get an irate, finger-wagging passenger somewhere half an hour ago, I hope you'll spare them a kind thought!

Disclaimer

I wish to acknowledge that, reading back through the book, I may possibly have been a little disingenuous towards the following people:

- Doctor Hilary – Helen says that I'm just jealous! Rubbish!
- London taxi drivers – So, by way of contrition, I am planning a national 'Hug a Cabbie' day to show just how much we appreciate them all!

One final point on cabbies: I don't know how true this is, but I once heard that whatever a person's default facial expression is up to the age of forty (happy, content, miserable as sin, etc.), thereafter, this expression becomes fixed for life. Just something for the young budding black taxi drivers to be mindful of!

- Alexander Armstrong – The thing about 'a crime against the ears of humanity' – only kidding! You should go a long way with that voice! And, just to let you know, I've already written my Christmas wish list!
- Americans.

Mary: once again, my sincerest gratitude to you for inspiring me to put my experiences and thoughts down in this book. I've thoroughly enjoyed the process, and know that I would never have done it without your encouragement! Thank you so much!

Well, it just remains for me to thank you for your company, and I hope that, one day, we may journey together in person and have a lovely chat. (Be warned, though, you might end up in the next volume!)

Finally, before I park up for the day, I have a confession I feel I have to make. Please bear with me, as this isn't going to be easy for me to do.

It was the Wednesday before last at around 7.10 pm. I'd been having one of those nightmare days – anything that could possibly go wrong, went wrong! My stress levels were through the roof and I felt completely deflated! And then, out of the blue, and I have absolutely no explanation at all for what came over me (the whole incident is a complete blur), without any warning at all, before I knew where I was, I'd texted in to Lynn Parsons at Magic FM for a personal mention! I wasn't really expecting any response from her, to be honest, and had all but forgotten about it, when at precisely 9.23 pm, to my total and utter astonishment, Lynn announced on air – *"Buck, a first-time texter to the show, you are very welcome here. Buck is a London minicab driver and is having a particularly bad day. We can all relate to that, can't we, guys? Buck, we know how challenging it can be driving around London, and we want you and all your colleagues to know that we really appreciate everything you do getting us where we need to be. So, relax, take a deep breath, this song is especially for you, Beverley Craven's* I'll Be Home Soon."

Wow, I felt embraced, like somebody actually understood my plight. It was as if Lynn had wrapped me up all nice and snoodly doodly in a soft, warm, fleecy blanket, and gently caressed all my cares and woes completely away!

Now I get it, and it felt good! REAL GOOD!

APPENDIX A

Answers to Quiz from Page 90.

1. How heavy was Gwen from Caerphilly when she was born on 2nd November 1976?

4lb 3oz

2. How heavy is Gwen from Caerphilly now?

Wouldn't be gentlemanly of me to say

3. Now a renowned entomologist, Lucy from Reigate, Surrey, first developed her fascination with insects at the tender age of nine when she befriended a daddy long legs in her father's allotment shed. Because of its distinctive gangly appearance, and the slow, cumbersome way that it moved around, scattered with occasional bursts of frenetic energy, what name did she give to that spider?

Dave

4. Jagdeep from Hayes in Middlesex is a successful investment banker on a six-figure salary, but, at the age of five, what did he want to be when he grew up?

A JCB driver at his local council tip

5. In 1969, to the delight of his parents, Rodric from Strathclyde was the first person in his family to pass his driving test. What was the make and model of his first car?

Hillman Imp

6. For a bonus point, what colour was that car?

Sort of silvery grey with a lime green trim